big load afloat

U.S. DOMESTIC WATER TRANSPORTATION RESOURCES

A publication of
THE AMERICAN WATERWAYS OPERATORS, INC.
1250 Connecticut Avenue • Suite 502 • Washington, D. C. 20036

Table Of Contents

THE BARGE AND TOWING INDUSTRY ASSOCIATION
A W O

Library of Congress Catalog Card No. 65-5774

First Printing—1965
Second Printing—1966
Third Printing—1973

Price: $7.50 hard cover copy; $4.50 soft cover copy.

Photographs used in this book were made available through the courtesy of various companies engaged in barge and towing vessel industry operations, the Army Corps of Engineers, United States Coast Guard, Tennessee Valley Authority, and others.

FOREWORD — *The internal water courses served as the routes of exploration and settlement of this land.*

These courses set the paths and roads for the early settlers; and the settlers chose sites on the water routes to establish their communities.

The water courses then became the transportation and communications links between communities.

The communities flourished; and commerce on the rivers and canals and in the harbors also flourished.

Most of our great centers of population, of industrial production and commercial distribution, and our centers of culture owe their origins and their initial growth to commerce on these internal water courses.

And they still depend today on these water courses for a great measure of their prosperity.

Thirty-eight of the 50 states, with almost 95 percent of the population, have commercial transportation services provided by vessels operating on rivers, canals, bays, sounds or lakes. One hundred thirty-one of the 150 cities having a population of 100,000 or more are located on commercial navigation channels.

1 Water Transport is a Business Builder

Most freight moving on U. S. inland waterways is carried in unmanned, non-self-propelled barges having drafts of six to 14 feet. Standard depth for inland navigation channels is nine feet. A small part of inland waterways service is provided by shallow-draft self-propelled freighting vessels and tankers, but the normal freighting equipment is the barge.

The barges are moved in groups or strings by towing vessels, either a towboat which is designed and operated to push the barges ahead, or a tug which is designed primarily to pull the barges on a hawser. In some instances, however, the tug may push the barges ahead or carry them alongside.

Shallow-draft water carrier operations provide service principally for the transportation of bulk-loading commodities—both dry and liquid—moving usually in barge-load lots of 500 to 3,000 tons per barge. There are ocean-going barges of more than 30,000 tons capacity.

The commodities particularly attracted to inland water-borne transportation are raw materials, moving in large quantities from one stage of production and processing to the next stage of finishing. Petroleum products, chemicals, grains, and coal, for example, lend themselves especially well to barge transportation. Many heavy, bulky semi-finished as well as finished products also move by barge. Barge transportation is an essential part of our mass production and marketing processes.

The economic value of this mode of transportation has been demonstrated and proven to many industries—mining, agriculture, petroleum, iron and steel, chemicals, aluminum, forest products, and the building trades in general. The Government's space program is dependent on barge service to transport the booster engines from production plants to test sites and launching sites.

Increasing demand for water transportation service has stimulated improvement of water channels as well as improvements in equipment and technology of operations. Barge service is safe and reliable. It is the lowest cost mode of transportation for the commodities for which it is adaptable.

Shippers use barge service to hold existing markets. They use it to expand their markets where the high costs of other modes may deny them access to outlets. And they use water transportation where possible in combination with rail and truck services to attain the most advantageous pattern of movement of raw materials for processing and for the distribution of finished products.

Water transportation requires less energy per ton-mile than any other method of freight distribution. Water freight requires 500 BTU's of energy for every ton-mile of freight moved, rail freight requires 750 BTU's per ton-mile, pipelines 1,850 BTU's per ton-mile, trucks 2,400 BTU's of energy per ton-mile and air cargo ~~6,300~~ 63,000 BTU's per ton-mile.

The barge and towing vessel industry has kept pace with shippers' needs, both as to equipment and service. Navigation techniques and aids have been developed which permit around-the-clock operations of towing vessels in all kinds of weather. Origin-to-destination speed is at an average of about six miles per hour, with some high-speed integrated tows making 15 miles per hour. The development and construction of barge equipment is keyed to shipper needs.

Because of these service characteristics, barge transportation has become a primary business growth stimulator.

2 A Growing National Resource

Barges—pushed by towboats or pulled by tugboats—and shallow-draft freighting vessels plying more than 25,000 miles of navigable inland channels carry 16 percent of the nation's domestic commerce.

A towboat or a tug may push or pull one barge or any multiple of barges ranging up to as many as 40 barges in push-towing operations or three or four in pull-towing operations, depending on the type of service and the characteristics of the waterway on which the tow is operating.

Cost of barge service to shippers averages three mills per ton-mile. For purposes of comparison: rail service costs the shipper more than five times as much—about 16 mills per ton-mile; truck service costs 8 cents per ton-mile; air freight service costs about 22½ cents per ton-mile. Some shippers get rail service for six or seven mills per ton-mile. Those who get it at this lower price

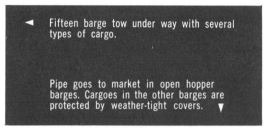

◄ Fifteen barge tow under way with several types of cargo.

Pipe goes to market in open hopper barges. Cargoes in the other barges are protected by weather-tight covers. ▼

Two integrated high-speed tows hauling petroleum products are shown on the Mississippi. The barges in such integrated units are constructed to achieve the underwater shape of a single vessel. Such units haul petroleum, petroleum products and chemicals. ►

do so not because of carrier generosity but because of competition and most often because of barge competition.

Low cost is the inherent advantage of water transportation.

To make inland water transportation publicly available the Federal Government, under Congressional authorizations dating back to the beginning of the Republic, provides, maintains, and operates a system of internal commercial navigation channels without charge to anyone for their use.

The Congress of the United States, as a part of national transportation policy, has declared that the inherent advantages of each mode of transportation shall be recognized and promoted "to the end of developing, coordinating, and preserving a national transportation system by water, highway, and rail, as well as other means. . . ."

Approximately *1,849 companies are engaged in commercial operations on the inland waters of the United States —**185 companies certificated by the Interstate Commerce Commission to provide service as regular route common carriers; **31 companies holding ICC permits to provide services under contracts with shippers; carriers hold both common and contract carrier rights; 1,629 companies engaged in the transportation of commodities which are exempt from regulation under provisions of the Interstate Commerce Act; and about 400 companies engaged in private transportation of their own commodities.

The 1,849 companies operate 17,527 dry cargo barges and scows with a total cargo capacity in excess of 19,710,605 tons; 3,420 tank barges with a total cargo capacity of approximately 7,486,718 tons; and 4,278 towboats and tugs with a total aggregate power in excess of 4,302,333 horsepower.

The physical plant of the shallow-draft water carrier industry as a whole is in excellent condition. It is made up of modern equipment. Fleet growth since World War II has followed a consistent, steady pattern of additions, modernizations and replacements of equipment to meet customer requirements. The fleet keeps pace with requirements in every respect.

The total investment of all for-hire carriers operating on the inland waters (exclusive of the Great Lakes) in carrier equipment only is estimated at more than $2 billion. This is exclusive of terminals and other shore-based equipment. The estimate also excludes the equipment of private carriers.

The industry is assured of a continuing source of investment funds, although it was not until recent years that the shallow-draft water carriers went to outside sources for financing. Because this has been a growth industry since the end of World War II, little difficulty has been experienced by carriers who have sought outside financing. They have found it through the normal channels of banks, other financial institutions and insurance companies. The loan departments of the more aggressive banking institutions are seeking opportunities to finance water carrier equipment. There is little investment-trust financing in the inland industry, although there has been evidence of interest on the part of financial institutions in this direction.

But inland water transportation is more than just another growth industry on the American scene. It is basically a part of a natural resource

* For a listing of individual companies, vessels operated, and type of operation see TRANSPORTATION SERIES, VOLUMES 3, 4 and 5 published by Corps of Engineers, U.S. Army, available from District Engineer, U.S. Army Engineers District, New Orleans, P. O. Box 60267, New Orleans

** As of 1972

▲ Tows like this move in excess of 213,551,179 tons of petroleum and petroleum products annually on U. S. inland waters.

The tug at left is pulling its tow of barges; that at right is pushing. They are on the Gulf Intracoastal Waterway, near Houma, Louisiana. ▼

▲ This towboat is under way with 28 barges loaded with a variety of commodities.

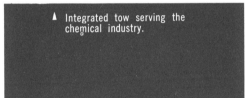

▲ Integrated tow serving the chemical industry.

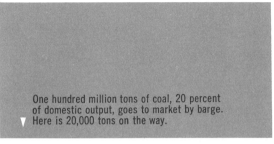

One hundred million tons of coal, 20 percent of domestic output, goes to market by barge. ▼ Here is 20,000 tons on the way.

which is not subject to depletion due to use. It is a growing resource in terms of its increasing contribution to the national economy. The water channels are true arteries of commerce. The benefits of low cost water carrier services extend throughout the trade areas of water-located communities. In many cases, it expands those trade areas.

Approximately 80,000 persons are employed aboard the inland fleet. An estimated equal number of persons are employed in shore-based work directly connected with inland fleet operations —office personnel, terminal operators, service personnel, and shipbuilding and ship repair personnel.

This modern inland fleet operates around the clock in all kinds of weather with the assistance of radar, radio-telephone communications, searchlights, depth finders, swing-o-meters, and other aids to navigation.

An important over-all effect of water transportation is to hold down the delivered cost of commodities—both the commodities transported in water-borne commerce and those transported by other modes competing directly with water-borne commerce.

Continuing technological advances will expand the opportunities for exploitation of the inherent cost advantage of water transport. Great improvement in service techniques has been accomplished in the last 15 to 25 years. Undoubtedly additional improvements can be made which will enhance the value of inland water carrier services to shippers. Some of the future improvements probably will come through coordination of services by the various modes and through some form of development of containerization adapted to combined service of inland water carriers with rail and highway operations.

3 From Keelboats to Towboats and Tugs

The first piece of transportation equipment to see service on our internal water courses was a canoe.

Then came the rafts—called flatboats or broad-horns. They were flat-bottomed and box-like, covered from bow to stern. They were one-way vessels for going downstream, propelled by the currents with little but guidance from their handlers.

The keelboat made its debut with the 19th century. It was a long, narrow vessel with graceful lines. It was a sturdily built two-way traveler—upstream as well as downstream. It carried as much as 80 tons of freight. For downstream hauls it needed only careful, skillful guidance. To propel it upstream men walked the river bank and pulled the keelboat with ropes or they stood aboard and pushed it by using iron-tipped poles that reached to the river bottom. One historian reported 500 keelboats on the Ohio River and its tributaries in 1819. The number on the Mississippi undoubtedly was far greater.

In 1811, just four years after the invention of the steamboat, the river steamer NEW ORLEANS was launched at Pittsburgh and went into service between there and New Orleans. By 1836, river steamboats were making calls at New Orleans at the rate of 1,000 per year. By 1852, the public landing at Cincinnati was reporting river steamboat calls at an annual rate of 8,000, about one per hour.

Traffic on the inland waterways expanded so rapidly with the development of the steamboat that Congress acted in 1824 to improve the rivers and harbors on a planned basis. The President was authorized to utilize the services of the Army Corps of Engineers for this work. Ever since that time, the Corps has had responsibility for the planning, improving, and maintaining of the nation's navigable waters, including harbors.

An Act of April 30, 1824 is of historic significance and reads in its entirety as follows:

"AN ACT TO PROCURE THE NECESSARY SURVEYS, PLANS, AND ESTIMATES, UPON THE SUBJECT OF ROADS AND CANALS.

"(Sect. 1.) Be it enacted by the Senate and House of Representatives of the United States of America, in Congress assembled, That the President of the United States is hereby authorized to cause the necessary surveys, plans, and estimates, to be made of the routes of such Roads and Canals as he may deem of national importance, in a commercial or military point of view, or necessary for the transportation of the public mail; designating, in the case of each canal, what parts may be made capable of sloop navigation: the surveys, plans, and estimates, for each, when completed, to be laid before Congress.

"(Sect. 2.) And be it further enacted, That, to carry into effect the objects of this act, the President be, and he is hereby authorized to employ two or more skillful civil engineers, and such officers of the Corps of Engineers, or who may be detailed to do duty with that Corps, as he may think proper; and the sum of thirty thousand dollars be, and the same is hereby appropriated, to be paid out of any moneys in the treasury, not otherwise appropriated."

Before 1824 river and harbor improvements were not coordinated and what was done was carried out by state and local agencies. Until that time the general practice was for the Treasury Department to make harbor surveys and coastal charts, and to erect lighthouses, public piers, beacons, and buoys.

▲ The use of barges was pioneered in the early packet boat era. Here an old packet, operating on the Warrior River in Alabama with a load of cotton, hauls barges alongside carrying more of the same cargo.

In 1952, one of the Ohio River's last steamboat races was held off Huntington, West Virginia. The Steamers E. D. Kenna and Charles R. Hook raced eight miles downstream, each pushing four empty barges. The Kenna, since broken up for scrap, won by 18 inches. ▼

Local governments and private interests benefiting from them usually executed local harbor improvements.

The first money appropriated by Congress for river improvements was made on May 24, 1824, in "An Act to Improve the Navigation of the Ohio and Mississippi Rivers." It granted $75,000 "for removing sand bars from the Ohio, and planters, sawyers and snags from the Mississippi." This was the first practical step under Federal responsibility for development of the nation's navigable channels.

The same year Congress also made its first appropriation for harbor improvement in "An Act making appropriations for deepening the channel leading into the Harbor of Presque Isle and for repairing Plymouth Beach." Congress set aside $20,000 for each of these projects, one on Lake Erie and the other on the New England Coast.

The incredibly rapid spread of a rail network over the nation, particularly after the War Between the States, dampened interest in waterways, but they were of vital importance to the growing nation for the first half of the last century.

At the height of the packet boat era in the United States just before the War Between the States, the river fleet was reportedly carrying more tonnage than that handled by all the vessels of the British Empire.

During the War Between the States, there was a constant struggle for control of the rivers and coastal waters serving the areas of conflict. Traffic in these waters was brought to a virtual standstill. Hundreds of steamboats were burned.

For all practical purposes, river transportation became a casualty of war. The fleet was not rebuilt. One of the reasons was the emergence of the railroads as the dominant form of transportation. In 1850 there were only 9,000 miles of rail lines in the United States; by 1890 the trackage had increased to almost 164,000 miles. Of devastating significance was the railroads' entry into water transportation. They bought up river lines and lake lines. They even bought some privately owned canals. Their purpose was not to promote water transportation, but to destroy it. The railroads used some water shipping lines as fighting ships to bleed competing water lines to death economically. Others were bought to let the vessels rot at their docks. And the docks and terminals rotted with them. Railroad-purchased canals were relegated to disuse. The railroads' tactics in this respect finally attracted the attention of Congress and in 1912 the Panama Canal Act was passed to divorce railroads from ownership of water carriers.

The early river fleet operated over completely natural channels. Although channel clearing was started with snagging operations on the Ohio River in

Transportation of oil by water was started in 1860 on the Allegheny River and Oil Creek in Pennsylvania. Barrels of oil were hauled on flatboats to Pittsburgh, the flatboats moving during periods of high water or with the help of artificial freshets. The first steamboat reached the oil fields in 1862, about the time this photograph was taken. ▶

1824, little improvement was made until after the turn of the century.

One of the early water courses was the Erie Canal, which was completed in 1825 and later became the New York State Barge Canal. The Erie brought New York City and its environs closer to the Middle West by a method of transportation that was about one-tenth of the cost of overland transportation in those days.

Except for local operations inland water transportation was largely stagnant from the end of the War Between the States until after World War I. President Theodore Roosevelt appointed the Inland Waterways Commission in 1907 to study the status of waterways and water carriers. This Commission recommended in 1908 that Congress make more suitable provision for improving the inland waterways of the United States.

The Panama Canal Act followed four years later and is considered by historians as the legislative keystone of the revival of inland waterways transportation. This Act prohibits railroads from owning, controlling or operating a water carrier that operates through the Panama Canal or elsewhere, provided, however, that in the case of a water carrier not operating through the Panama Canal authority is conferred upon the Interstate Commerce Commission to make a determination as to whether such ownership or operation will be in the public interest and will not exclude, prevent or reduce competition on the route.

As might be expected, passage of the Act did not result in immediate divorcement of railroads from ownership of water carriers. The litigation that followed did however except in some cases where the water operations were considered auxiliary to rail services.

In 1959-1962 a major test of the Act was made. The Illinois Central and Southern Pacific Railroads in 1959 filed

One of the forerunners of modern river transportation was the steamer Spread Eagle of Eagle Packet Company, Quincy, Illinois, of 1873 vintage. ▼

▲ The stern-wheel towboat is almost a curiosity today. A few do remain in service. This particular one was recently retired.

an application with the Interstate Commerce Commission seeking approval to acquire the John I. Hay Company barge line, a major common carrier operating on the Mississippi River System and the Gulf Intracoastal Waterway. This was the first major effort by railroads to invade domestic water carrier operations since passage of the Panama Canal Act. The American Waterways Operators, Inc., opposed the application, as did other interests. In 1962, ICC denied the application in a decision reaffirming the established public policy of separation of ownership and operation of the various transport modes.

Periodic attempts have been made by the railroads to get in the barge business since this time.

To help meet wartime demands in 1918 a Federal manager was appointed to commandeer and put into operation as soon as possible all available equipment capable of being used for the transportation of freight on the rivers and canals. The Transportation Act of 1920 declared the intent of Congress to promote, encourage, and develop water transportation. Four years later the Inland Waterways Corporation was incorporated by the Congress as a pioneering operation to demonstrate the transportation capabilities of modern towboats and barges. Historians generally date the beginnings of modern inland water carrier operations at about this period.

4 The Vessels and the Men Aboard

What the vessels are not—they are not pretty in the esthetic sense. They are not picturesque as were the sternwheelers that Mark Twain glamorized. Neither do they have the glamorous bigness of ocean-going vessels.

What they are—they are the most efficient transporters of freight in existence.

The barges are unimpressive to look upon except for their austere bigness. But to a shipper who knows how safely, economically and smoothly they ride the waters to produce 3-mills-per-ton-mile transportation they have a kind of beauty all their own. The average barge can carry about five times its own weight. No other type of freight vehicle compares with it in this measure of efficiency.

The towboats which provide the power to move the barges have a business-like appearance in keeping with the stark efficiency of the barges.

Towboats are square on the bow and almost square on the stern with somewhat clumsy-looking uprights at the bow. They appear to squat low in the water, the water almost lapping the deck. But a towboat wears an air of power and authority. The clumsy-looking uprights at the bow are towing knees. They are pusher plates against which barges are snugged and securely lashed.

Tied together, barge on barge, and in turn lashed to the towing knees of the power unit, they form a tow that looks and acts like a single vessel. One towboat and one barge may make a tow. One towboat and 10 barges, or 20 barges, or 30, or even 40 barges may make a tow. And the snub-nosed, squat towboat translates its power and authority into action to move the tow, to steer it, to control it. In movement a tow becomes a thing of beauty—one kind of beauty to an observer, another to a skilled river pilot, still another to a shipper getting transportation at a cost which enables him to hold his markets, to broaden and expand them.

The tugboat resembles the towboat only in power and efficiency. It has a shaped bow, sits higher in the water,

▲ Typical big, modern river towboat, one of several types operated on the Mississippi River System.

and has a racy look about it. It hauls barges astern on a hawser, or snugs them up against the hip, or slips its bow into a slot between two of them, or even slips its bow into a built-in V slot in the stern of a barge. And tugs shove ocean liners and freighters around in a working display of their power in harbor operations. The tugs do the open water towing of barges—on the intracoastal canals, in the Gulf of Mexico, off the Atlantic and Pacific Coasts, and in trade to and from Alaska and Hawaii. They are rugged, dependable, low-cost transporters like the towboats.

Together the barges, the towboats, and the tugs make a unique transportation team. Operating on water level routes it is not the fastest nor the most flexible mode of transportation we have, but for sheer efficiency in the movement of vast tonnages of freight it has no peer.

5 Towboats and Tugboats

Towboats and tugboats form an indispensable team in U. S. transportation.

Built to the most precise design specifications, and equipped with the most modern navigational instruments and safety devices, there is little to relate modern towboats to their ancestors—the stern and side wheeler steamboats that once sailed the rivers in great numbers.

The powerful towboats ply the protected inland rivers and canals, serving as the power units to move barges which supply a substantial portion of the transportation needs of industrialized America. Towboat is a misnomer, incidentally, since it pushes rather than pulls barges.

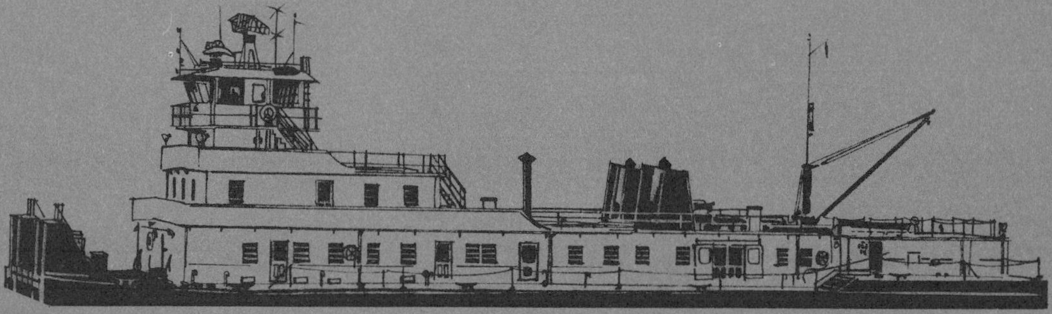

TOWBOATS

Length Feet	Breadth Feet	Draft Feet	Horsepower
117	30	7.6	1000 to 2000
142	34	8	2000 to 4000
160	40	8.6	4000 to 6000

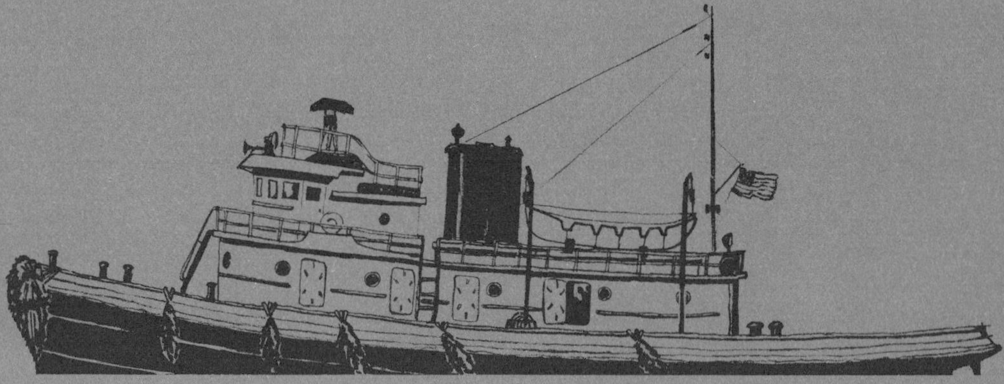

TUGBOATS

Length Feet	Breadth Feet	Draft Feet	Horsepower
65 to 80	21 to 23	8	350 to 650
90	24	10 to 11	800 to 1200
95 to 105	25 to 30	12 to 14	1200 to 3500
125 to 150	30 to 34	14 to 15	2000 to 4500

The tugboat serves the same purpose in many instances but it is designed and used for open water towing of barges where it is subjected to and can take the forces of heavy wind and wave action.

While tugboats are widely used to tow barges for general freighting services along the intracoastal canals, on the Great Lakes, and in the open seas, they are perhaps best known for their work in the coastal harbors where they dock and undock oceangoing vessels, assist in bunkering, perform lighterage work, and do general harbor towing. They also perform much specialized work in towing dredges, pile drivers, derrick barges, offshore oil exploration barges, oil well drilling rigs, and compressor barges. Oceangoing towing jobs of all kinds are handled by tugs, as are all types of salvage work.

Each type is classified as a towing vessel, but the towboat and tugboat are vastly different. The tug has a shaped bottom, as against the towboat's almost flat-bottomed hull. Tugs require sealed watertight doors and port holes to prevent entry of water; while the towboat has conventional doors and windows.

The tug in effect is an oceangoing vessel, used most extensively in open water service, whereas the towboat is used exclusively on the rivers and other protected, relatively calm water courses.

There is a wide variety of towboats plying the nation's waterways today. They range from vessels with single screws to vessels with four propellers with each screw driven by an individual diesel engine. Some come small in overall dimensions approximating 36 feet long, 12 feet wide, six feet draft, with engines of about 100 horsepower. The largest towboat is 170 feet long, 58 feet wide, with draft of 10 feet 3 inches. This vessel has four screws with engines that develop up to 9,000 horsepower. Towboats of 6,000 horsepower and up are capable of pushing barges carrying as much as 40,000 to 50,000 tons of cargo. In comparison, a modern diesel freight locomotive of 6,000 horsepower can handle efficiently a train of 120 cars loaded to an average of 50 tons per car, a total of approximately 6,000 tons.

Three of the most common sizes of towboats being built today have these general dimensions:

- 117 feet long, 30 feet wide, 7.6 feet draft, 1,000 to 2,000 horsepower
- 142 feet long, 34 feet wide, 8 feet draft, 2,000 to 4,000 horsepower
- 160 feet long, 40 feet wide, 8.6 feet draft, 4,000 to 6,000 horsepower.

For towboats of greater horsepower the dimensions can range up to 200 feet long, 55 feet wide, 8.6 feet draft. Several towboats are now under construction of 10,000 horsepower and will be largest in the inland fleet when they go into operation. These particular vessels, costing about $3 million each, will be 190 feet long, 54 feet wide with 8.6 feet draft.

Tugboats also come in a variety of sizes. Average dimensions are:

- 65 to 80 feet long, 21 to 23 feet wide, 8 feet draft, 350 to 650 horsepower
- 90 feet long, 24 feet wide, 10 to 11 feet draft, 800 to 1,200 horsepower
- 95 to 105 feet long, 25 to 30 feet wide, 12 to 14 feet draft, 1,200 to 3,500 horsepower
- 125 to 150 feet long, 30 to 34 feet wide, 14 to 15 feet draft, 2,000 to 4,500 horsepower.

▲ Tunnel stern feature of towboat is shown in this photograph.

▲ Tug pushes a tank barge.

▲ This tug is moving two rail carfloats, each capable of carrying 20 railroad cars.

Tug takes ocean liner into port. ▼

This is a harbor boat. ▼

To Push or to Pull?

Generally the type of water determines which of two methods of towing is used—push-towing or pull-towing—and therefore the type of power unit, either towboat or tug.

On most of the inland systems where the water routes are protected by surrounding land masses and where the waters are relatively calm either in their natural state (as on the lower Mississippi and the Missouri Rivers), or where a system of locks and dams creates relative calmness, the towboat is used for push-towing operations. For push-towing the barges are tied rigidly together by steel cables or ropes to form a single unit, and this unit is then lashed solidly against the boat's towing knees. The power unit working at the rear of the tow can handle a greater number of barges at greater speed under more absolute control than can be handled in pull-towing operations. The relatively flat-bottomed towboat with massive power in its propellers also has a set of multiple rudders which afford maximum control for forward, backing, and flanking movements such as are required to navigate the restricted channels of the rivers and canals.

◄ This is the business end of a towboat with four propellers, each geared to a diesel engine. Note the rudders fore and aft of the propellers which provide the steering control that enables a pilot to guide a long string of barges ahead of the boat.

One of the two most powerful towboats in the world. This 9,000 horsepower vessel operates on the Lower Mississippi River. ▼

▲ Towboat pushes barges, each loaded with 400 cords of pulpwood.

Character of the waterway, condition of the waterway, lockage conditions, size of tow, and horsepower of the towing vessel in relation to the size of tow all influence origin-to-destination running times of towboats. The following are typical transit times for the average tow over typical inland routes under ideal conditions:

- Pittsburgh-New Orleans, 1,852 miles: upstream 14 days and 2 hours; downstream 8 days and 18 hours
- Cincinnati-New Orleans, 1,380 miles: upstream 10 days and 19 hours; downstream 6 days and 7 hours
- St. Louis-New Orleans, 1,053 miles: upstream 8 days and 19 hours; downstream 4 days and 9 hours
- Kansas City-New Orleans, 1,434 miles: upstream 11 days and 22 hours; downstream 6 days
- Minneapolis-New Orleans, 1,731 miles: upstream 13 days and 12 hours; downstream 7 days and 22 hours
- Chicago-New Orleans, 1,418 miles: upstream 11 days and 8 hours; downstream 6 days and 7 hours
- Pittsburgh-Houston (via New Orleans), 2,257 miles: upstream 16 days and 21 hours; downstream 10 days and 20 hours

- Pittsburgh-Houston (via Atchafalaya River), 2,186 miles; upstream 16 days and 6 hours; downstream 10 days and 14 hours
- St. Louis-Houston (via New Orleans), 1,458 miles: upstream 11 days and 4 hours; downstream 6 days and 12 hours
- St. Louis-Houston (via Atchafalaya River), 1,387 miles: upstream 10 days and 23 hours; downstream 6 days and 6 hours
- Cincinnati-Houston (via New Orleans), 1,785 miles: upstream 13 days and 15 hours; downstream 8 days and 10 hours
- Cincinnati-Houston (via Atchafalaya River), 1,714 miles: upstream 12 days and 23 hours; downstream 8 days and 3 hours
- Chicago-Houston (via New Orleans), 1,823 miles: upstream 14 days and 3 hours; downstream 8 days and 10 hours
- Chicago-Houston (via Atchafalaya River), 1,752 miles: upstream 13 days and 12 hours; downstream 8 days and 3 hours
- Minneapolis-Houston (via New Orleans), 2,136 miles: upstream 16 days and 7 hours; downstream 10 days and 1 hour
- Minneapolis-Houston (via Atchafalaya River), 2,065 miles: upstream 15 days and 16 hours; downstream 9 days and 18 hours
- Pittsburgh-Brownsville (via New Orleans), 2,542 miles: upstream 18 days and 21 hours; downstream 12 days and 8 hours
- Pittsburgh-Brownsville (via Atchafalaya River), 2,471 miles: upstream 18 days and 6 hours; downstream 12 days and 2 hours
- Chicago-Brownsville (via New Orleans), 2,108 miles: upstream 16 days and 3 hours; downstream 9 days and 21 hours
- Chicago-Brownsville (via Atchafalaya River), 2,037 miles: upstream 15 days and 12 hours; downstream 9 days and 15 hours

Wind, wave, and tidal actions will break up a tow of vessels lashed rigidly together as is done for push-towing. Where these conditions exist, the pull-towing method is used in which a tug hauls barges behind on a hawser. These conditions exist on some portions of the navigable inland waterways, particularly sections of the Gulf Intracoastal Waterway and Atlantic Intracoastal Waterway. This method of operations naturally prevails in towing vessel operations which are being employed to an increasing extent on the Gulf of Mexico, along the Pacific Coast, to some extent along the Atlantic Coast, and between the Pacific Coast and Alaska and Hawaii.

There is a limit to the number of barges which may be pulled on a hawser, however, and it is obvious that a towing vessel can exercise little guidance control over barges being pulled except to provide propulsion power. Tugboats are rigged for this work.

Many towboats are now being placed in service rigged for both push-towing and pull-towing. To rig a towboat for pull-towing requires only the addition of a towing bitt located ahead of the steering rudders. However, towboats are limited as to the waters on which they can work. They are not built for sea duty.

Power and Control

Practically the entire fleet of towboats and tugboats is powered by diesel engines. The steam-powered vessel is a relic of the past and only a very few of them are left in service. The complete shift from steam to diesel propulsion when once started in towboats and tugs took place very rapidly.

The diesel towboat which replaced the stern wheeler on the rivers and canals and in the harbors is responsible for bringing the barge and towing vessel industry to its place of national prominence on the transportation scene in the last 25 years.

The development of the diesel-powered towboat and tug has produced the most efficient application of power in any mode of transportation. The great service gain is the result of applying maximum usable power to the task of moving freight, applying it with the greatest possible efficiency, and keeping the power unit at work a greater percentage of the time.

The adoption of the propeller as a replacement for the stern wheel or side wheel on river and canal boats immediately posed the problem of a limitation on the size of the propeller imposed by the small space between the bottom of the boat and the bottom of the channel. This problem has been met in two ways: the development of more efficient propellers; and the development and perfection in towboats of the tunnel stern. The tunnel stern is a design feature in which part of the propeller is actually above the level of the water surface in a spoon-shaped recess in the bottom of the hull which is filled with water by vacuum action when the propeller is turning. Another device has been introduced to river towboats to improve propeller efficiency. This is the Kort nozzle, a funnel-shaped structure built around the propeller to concentrate the flow of water to the propeller. Under certain favorable operating conditions the Kort nozzle is reported to add as much as 25 percent thrust to the propeller.

▲ Towboat under construction showing its two propellers. Rudders have not yet been installed.

▲ This twin-screw towboat is equipped with Kort nozzles to concentrate the flow of water to the propellers and give added efficiency.

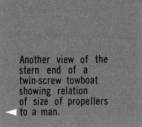

Another view of the stern end of a twin-screw towboat showing relation of size of propellers ◄ to a man.

One of the most important gains in efficiency was the development, principally during World War II, of dependable reversing-reduction gears capable of transmitting high horsepower. Before these gears were available, the conflict between high engine efficiency at high RPM's and high propeller efficiency at low RPM's, usually resulted in a sacrifice of efficiency at both ends. Good reversing-reduction gears permit engine operation at the most efficient RPM. Propellers are designed for whatever RPM can use the horsepower most efficiently within the available diameter.

An added benefit of the improved power trains is the adaptability of such installations to the use of pilothouse controls which permit faster and more accurate handling of the engines with resulting time-savings in maneuvering.

One of the greatest unsolved problems in gaining maximum efficiency from diesel propulsion on the inland waterways is the variation in load on the engine which is brought about by differences in size of tows, and by variations in the depth of water. Among the techniques which are being tried to cope with this problem are diesel-electric drive, controllable pitch propellers, and overload limiters.

In the continuing work to improve efficiency, hull design is receiving added attention through exhaustive tests of towed and self-propelled models in testing basins.

The exigencies of navigation in and out of the Chicago area with its multitude of very low bridges has produced the telescoping pilothouse design. The pilot, behind a tow of barges which themselves just clear the bridges, can lower his pilothouse to go under bridges and then immediately come up again to see ahead for navigation. This design, peculiar to the Chicago waterways, mounts the pilothouse and all the electrical and mechanical controls necessary to operate the boat on a hydraulic ram.

The telescoping pilothouse is an innovation dictated by the existence of low bridges which had been built over the waterways in the Chicago area before barge and towboat operations reached their present capacity. The telescoping pilothouse is not desirable for normal operations. It sacrifices working and living space, adds to construction and maintenance costs, and reduces both the efficiency and safety of the vessel.

In the pilothouse of a modern towboat the controls and aids to navigation reflect intensive application of modern science.

Electric steering controls which actuate huge hydraulic steering rams instantly align the two separate sets of rudders, one set forward and one set aft of the propellers. The setting of the steering levers by the pilot is a fingertip operation.

One thumb-sized lever for each engine is a combination clutch, gear shift, and throttle, and instantly provides the engine speed, power output and direction the pilot wants.

Finger-tip electrical controls direct the probing of the three-mile beam from each of two or three powerful arc lights.

Communications and Navigation

A powerful directional bull horn on top of the pilothouse sends the pilot's voice to the deckhands working out on the tow or to a man on shore half a mile away.

The pilot is in instant communication with any part of the vessel through his intercom system and by direct line to the mate supervising work out on the tow. Walkie-talkie radio is in wide use for communications between the pilothouse and the deck crew, between vessels and movable bridges over the waterways, between vessels and locks, and from vessel to vessel.

Tugs take freighter out of harbor to begin her sea voyage. ►

Tug pushes oil barge with her bow fitted into stern slot. ▼

Tug pulls barge loaded with pulpwood en route to paper mill. ►

Barge of 6,000 ton capacity starts voyage from Seattle, Washington, to Alaska carrying vans, automobiles and trucks. ►

Powerful tugs shift an ocean liner in harbor work. ▼

The propeller of this tug is encased in a nozzle which will concentrate the flow of water and increase the efficiency of operation. ►

The pilot talks to the office or to his home through the short-range radiophone connected into the land-line system. Where the short-range stations are too far from the river, he picks up the long-range phone and talks to a station a thousand miles away.

When he is not using his long-range radio, he keeps it tuned in on the intership channel. All other towboats do the same, and consequently long before two approaching boats are within sight of each other or close enough to exchange passing signals by whistle, the two pilots have made radio contact, discussed the navigating conditions involved in their passing, and have agreed how they will pass.

Efficient communications are an essential tool in inland water transportation. Dependable communications between company offices and towing vessels result in better dispatching of traffic as one ingredient of achieving greater shipper satisfaction; better utilization of equipment and therefore more economical operations; greater safety of vessel personnel, equipment and cargoes; and a measure of added personnel benefit to crews on long voyages away from their home port because it affords them a means of contact with their families when needed.

The radiotelephone is the communications lifeline of the shallow-draft industry. Most towing vessels are equipped with one or more radio sets operating on various frequency ranges assigned by the Federal Communications Commission.

The primary means of communications in the barge and towing industry are radiotelephone systems operating in the AM frequencies and single band frequencies below 30 MHz, and VHF maritime frequencies in coastal areas and the Western Rivers.

In many areas considerable interference exists in the medium range AM maritime frequency bands. Reasons for this include insufficient channels to accommodate the communications load, and the long distance propagation characteristics of these frequency bands. On the other hand, VHF with its limited range, greater channel availability, and its frequency modulation characteristics, can give superior short-range service. The Federal Communications Commission has made 41 frequencies (156 MHz to 162 MHz) available for assignment to ship stations in the VHF maritime mobile services. Of these, five are dedicated frequencies: one each for distress safety and calling, intership safety, navigation (bridge-to-bridge), environmental and state control. The others are allocated to port operations (seven); commercial ship-to-ship and ship-to-coast (12); non-commercial recreation (eight), and public correspondence (nine).

Until recent years, major reliance for radiotelephone communications was placed on AM equipment operating in the 2 to 3 megahertz band for intership communications and in the 2, 4, 6 and 8 MHz band for ship-to-ship communications. These frequencies are still used, but increasing use is now being made of VHF, which is basically for line-of-sight transmission, and single sideband systems. Under FCC Rules, double sideband systems operating on frequencies between 4 and 22 MHz must be converted to single sideband by January 1, 1974; and, in the band 2000 to 2850 kHz by January 1, 1977.

The desirable objective from a communications standpoint is to have fast, reliable radiotelephone service as free from interference as possible with towing vessels having the ability to communicate with each other, with other types of vessels using the waterways and harbors, with their offices either directly or through a land-based network, with river locks, and with movable bridges.

The few medium range AM frequencies available do not completely satisfy inland maritime communications needs.

From a safety and communications standpoint one of the most important statutes to be enacted in recent years was Public Law 92-63 "to require a radiotelephone on certain vessels while navigating on specified waters of the United States," which became effective on January 1, 1973.

This Act, which the barge and towing vessel industry unanimously supported in the interest of safety, is designed "to provide a positive means whereby the operators of approaching vessels can communicate their intentions to one another through voice radio, located convenient to the operator's navigation station."

The Act applies to

"(1) every power-driven vessel of three hundred gross tons and upward while navigating;

"(2) every vessel of one hundred gross tons and upward carrying one or more passengers for hire while navigating;

"(3) every towing vessel of 26 feet or over in length while navigating; and

"(4) every dredge and floating plant engaged in or near a channel or fairway in operations likely to restrict or affect navigation of other vessels."

Under provisions of the Act each of these vessels "shall have a radiotelephone capable of operation from its navigational bridge, or, in the case of a dredge, from its main control station and capable of transmitting and receiving on the frequency or frequencies within the 156-162 VHF megahertz band using the classes of emission designated by the Federal Communications Commission, after consultation with

▲ Tug approaching Honolulu Harbor with tandem barge loads of bins full of fresh pineapple en route to a cannery in Honolulu from the pineapple fields on one of Hawaii's outside islands.

other cognizant agencies, for the exchange of navigation information."

When it is foggy or rainy or when the snow flies, the pilot of a river or

One of the fleet of river towboats that produce efficient low-cost transportation service.

This is one of the big towboats that produce low-cost service on the Mississippi River System.

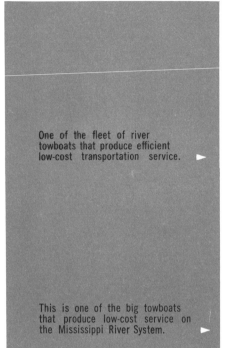

A triple-screw towboat, 164 feet long, 44 feet wide, with 10 foot draft, rests on marine railway prior to its launching.

Tug built for push-towing or pull-towing on the Gulf Intracoastal Waterway.

canal towboat no longer has to tie up. Radar presents him with a constant map of the river showing his position with relation to the shape of the river and any object in it. So helpful is this radar reference map that most pilots use it for checks even on clear nights.

In doubtful waters and particularly in bad visibility the pilot leans heavily on radar. He also finds an indispensable aid in the depth-finder which, working through a transceiver suspended in the water from the head of the tow, continually records the depth of the water on a tape in the pilothouse.

When fog shuts out visibility entirely and the pilot is groping through narrow waters with the aid of radar and the depth-finder, he also has a swing indicator to tell him the second his tow starts to drop off course. Thus he can apply corrective rudder even before the deviation shows on radar.

The use of the automatic pilot is becoming popular as a more accurate steering device when visual steering ability is restricted. In clear weather the automatic pilot, carefully used, will steer the tow with less rudder angle—and consequently give more miles per hour.

6 Barges

Virtually any commodity can be shipped by water. The inland waterways industry has implemented this theory by developing a variety of types and sizes of barges for the efficient handling of products ranging from coal in open hopper barges to chemicals in "thermos bottle" barges, and from dredged rock in dump scows to railroad cars on carfloats. And barging is the only practical mode for long distance moving of out-sized machinery, tanks, kilns, and some of the space vehicles.

Speed is important to the barge line operator. So the underwater hull shapes

◄ Typical hopper barge with rolling weather-tight hatch covers

and operating features of barges receive the same attention from the naval architect as does the modern high powered diesel towboat. Combined testing of towboat and barge models in experimental tanks in the United States and Europe often result in technological improvement of barge hull lines. Shipboard equipment is subject to the same theories of automation as any shoreside operation.

Twenty-five years ago most river barges were designed as single individual units, having a rake, or slope, on each end. For navigating singly, this form is still most efficient. However, model testing showed that the assembly of multiple units of this form in a single tow resulted in great loss of efficiency by the cumulative drag of many water-breaking rakes in the middle of the tow.

Some barges are designed to be assembled into integrated tows having an underwater shape that is nearly the equivalent of a single vessel. Such an integrated assembly made up of several vessels has a lead barge with an easy rake at the bow to minimize the resistance of the water. This lead barge has a square stern for joining with the square end of another barge, thus eliminating any underwater surface break. The trailing barge in an integrated assembly has a short rake on the stern. The bow of this barge will be square. Between the lead barge and the trailing barge, double square ended barges are inserted. The water resistance of such an integrated tow is nearly equivalent to the smooth underwater lines of a single vessel of equivalent total length. A premium benefit is the increase in capacity due to the added buoyancy of the square ends of the barges.

The integrated high speed tow is generally efficient for the carriage of a large volume of a single commodity over a long distance on a continuing basis. Identical draft of all barges comprising the tow is vital to the efficiency of the operation. They have been most success-

A 7,500 horsepower towboat with a 36-barge tow on the Mississippi River System. ►

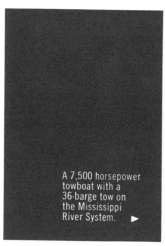

This 9,500-ton capacity sea-going barge has hydraulic self-stowing hatch covers that fold and pivot automatically to a vertical position. Note slot in stern for bow of tug when pushing.

The National Aeronautics and Space Administration's barge "Promise" en route on the Mississippi River carrying the Saturn space vehicle's big booster from Huntsville, Alabama, to Cape Kennedy, Florida.

The National Aeronautics and Space Administration's barge "Palaemon" was especially constructed to transport the 72-ton Saturn booster from the construction site at Huntsville, Alabama, to the launching site at Cape Kennedy, Florida. It moved 2,200 miles via the Tennessee, Ohio, Mississippi Rivers, and Gulf of Mexico. The space vehicle booster was too large for movement by any means other than barge.

fully used for transporting petroleum and petroleum products, chemicals and other liquids where they can be continuously operated as a unit.

The fully integrated design concept, however, has the disadvantage that a single barge built for an intermediate position in such a tow, square on both ends, is extremely unwieldy to handle when separated from the other units of the tow, especially in a current. Such barges are difficult to move around in terminal areas. The water resistance of these barges if placed in a tow with other barges which do not have matching square ends makes such use of them prohibitive.

There is a useful and successful compromise with the concept of the fully integrated tow. This produces a barge with a well designed rake on one end and square on the other end. Two such barges assembled square-end to square-end provide about eight percent increased capacity over two similar barges having rakes at each end. At ordinary towing speeds they have about 18 percent less resistance. By assembling such semi-integrated barges into fleets the combined effect of added ca-

Typical open hopper barge in use on rivers and canals.

Concrete pipe conduit sections are loaded into an open hopper barge.

pacity and less resistance permits a typical boat moving a typical tow of such barges to make about 25 percent more cargo ton-miles per hour than the same boat with the same tow of barges having a rake on each end. At the same time, by having a rake on one end these semi-integrated barges can be handled singly without difficulty.

Hopper Barges

Most versatile, least costly, and most numerous in the U. S. inland fleet is the hopper barge. With minor modifications it can be adapted to the transportation of literally any solid commodity in bulk or package.

The hopper barge is basically a simple double-skinned, open-top box, the inner shell forming a long hopper or cargo hold. The bottom, sides and ends of the hold are free of appendages and adapt ideally to unloading with clamshell buckets, hooks, grabs, continuous belt buckets, or pneumatic devices. They can accommodate dry bulk-loading commodities, structures and shapes, and heavy bulky vehicles with equal facility.

OPEN HOPPER BARGES

Length Feet	Breadth Feet	Draft Feet	Capacity Tons
175	26	9	1000
195	35	9	1500
290	50	9	3000

COVERED DRY CARGO BARGES

Length Feet	Breadth Feet	Draft Feet	Capacity Tons
175	26	9	1000
195	35	9	1500

LIQUID CARGO (TANK) BARGES

Length Feet	Breadth Feet	Draft Feet	Capacity Tons	Capacity Gallons*
175	26	9	1000	302,000
195	35	9	1500	454,000
290	50	9	3000	907,200

* Based on an average of 7.2 barrels per ton and 42 gallons per barrel.

Open Hopper Barges

The open hopper barge is a multi-purpose vessel in general use throughout the United States for the transportation of a wide range of commodities that need no protection from the elements.

Open hoppers serve the coal industry, moving in excess of 100 million tons a year, approximately one-fifth of the total output of U. S. mines. Coal accounts for about 23 percent of the total tonnage moving in inland waterways transportation. Open hoppers serve the steel industry and the aluminum industry with equal facility, moving both raw materials and finished products. They serve the construction industry in the movement of sand, gravel, crushed rock, limestone, sea shells, logs, lumber and lumber products. They serve the agricultural community in the movement of fertilizer materials. Heavy equipment and machinery and outsized tanks and pressure vessels are transported in open hopper barges.

There are three popular sizes of open hopper barges: one of 1,000-ton capacity, 175 feet long by 26 feet wide with nine-foot draft; one of 1,500-ton capacity, 195 feet long by 35 feet wide with a draft of nine feet; and one of 3,000-ton capacity, 290 feet long by 50 feet wide with a draft of nine feet. It should be noted that the capacities mentioned are usually maximum.

They are generally of welded plate construction, usually with double bottoms for greater safety. They are braced to resist the heaviest of external blows as well as to absorb the impact of loading and unloading buckets.

Covered Dry Cargo Barges

The covered dry cargo barge serves a wide variety of shippers throughout the United States in providing transportation for bulk-loading commodities that need protection from the elements.

Generally these vessels differ from the open hopper barge only in that they are equipped with watertight covers over the entire cargo hold.

Several types of covers have been developed.

Lift-type covers can be adapted to any hopper barge without modification of the barge itself. Such covers are handled by shoreside facilities, and when not in use can be stacked at the ends of the barge. This type cover is ideal for barges operating in both grain and ore service, for instance, since each of the several covers can be equipped with small hinged grain hatches so that cargo can be loaded and unloaded with grain legs or pneumatic devices without removing the hold covers.

Rolling covers, although more costly, are also more versatile. One telescoping type, where the covers roll fore and aft on tracks installed on the barge, permit the opening of one-half of the hopper at a time. Some variations of the rolling hatch cover permit opening of the entire hopper.

Covered dry cargo barges are used for the carriage of such commodities as grain and grain products, coffee, soybeans, paper and paper products, lumber and building materials, cement, iron and steel products, dry chemicals, aluminum and aluminum products, machinery and parts, rubber and rubber products, salt, soda ash, sugar, and in some cases packaged goods.

Two popular sizes of covered dry cargo barges are in general use. One of 1,000-ton capacity which has a length of 175 feet, breadth of 26 feet, and draft of nine feet; and one of 1,500-ton capacity with a length of 195 feet, breadth of 35 feet, and draft of nine feet.

One new design for covered dry cargo barges involves a 200′ by 35′ by 12′ depth dry cargo box barge with a capacity of 1,650 tons on nine-feet draft.

▲ Giant independent cylindrical tanks are nested into barges for the transportation of chemicals.

These vessels, like the open hoppers, are generally of welded steel construction.

Tank Barges

Three basic types of tank barges are used for the transportation of liquid commodities.

Single skin tank barges have bow and stern compartments separated from the midship by transverse collision bulkheads. The entire midship shell of the vessel constitutes the cargo tank. Hydrodynamic considerations require that this huge tank be divided by bulkheads. The hull structural framing is inside the cargo tank.

Double skin tank barges have, as the term implies, an inner and outer shell. The inner shell forms cargo tanks free of appendages and they are thus easy to clean and to line. Poisons and other hazardous liquids require the protection of the void compartments between the outer and inner shells.

Barges having independent cylindrical tanks are used to transport liquids under pressure or in cases where pressure is to be used to discharge the cargo. Cylindrical tank barge design is used in some cases to carry cargoes at or near atmospheric pressures because of the high efficiency of linings and/or insulation which can be incorporated. Cylindrical cargo tanks are generally mounted in the barge hopper and are thus free to expand or contract independent of the hull structure. For this reason, too, they are preferred for high temperature

◄ Molten sulphur pours into a barge for shipment. It will be kept heated and liquefied en route to its destination.

▲ Typical tank barges used to transport petroleum and petroleum products on inland waterways.

cargoes such as liquid sulphur at 280 degrees Fahrenheit, or refrigerated cargoes such as anhydrous ammonia at minus 28 degrees Fahrenheit.

Three popular sizes of tank barges (with maximum capacities noted) are:

- 1,000-ton capacity (302,000 gallons); length, 175 feet; breadth, 26 feet; draft, nine feet.
- 1,500-ton capacity (454,000 gallons); length, 195 feet; breadth, 35 feet; draft, nine feet.
- 3,000-ton capacity (907,200 gallons); length, 290 feet; breadth, 50 feet; draft, nine feet.

More than 3,185 tank barges with a total cargo capacity of almost 6,330,298 tons are in service. The majority are used for the transportation of petroleum and petroleum products, handling approximately 214,000,000 tons annually.

Since 1946, movements of bulk chemicals by barge have been increasing steadily and chemicals now comprise one of the largest movements of liquid commodities by water. The U.S. Coast Guard lists approximately 400 chemical commodities transported or proposed for transport by barge. Anhydrous ammonia is transported under pressure of 250 pounds per square inch or refrigerated to minus 28 degrees Fahrenheit.

Liquefied sulphur is moved at 260 to 280 degrees Fahrenheit. Liquefied methane is transported at minus 258 degrees

DECK BARGES

Length Feet	Breadth Feet	Draft Feet	Capacity Tons
110	26	6	350
130	30	7	900
195	35	8	1200

CARFLOATS

			Capacity Railroad Cars
257	40	10	10
366	36	10	19

SCOWS

Length Feet	Breadth Feet	Draft Feet	Capacity Tons
90	30	9	350
120	38	11	1000
130	40	12	1350

Fahrenheit. Barge-mounted tanks are used to transport liquid hydrogen at minus 423 degrees Fahrenheit and liquid oxygen at minus 297 degrees Fahrenheit.

The chemical industry makes significant use of barge transportation. The following is a partial list of products now being transported: acetic acid; acetic anhydride; tartaric acid; organic acids and anhydrides; hydrochloric acid; chromic acid; nitric acid; inorganic acids and anhydrids; acetone; butyl acetate; carbon bisulfide; formaldehyde or formalin; collecting reagents for concentration of ores, metals, or minerals; cellulose nitrate, wet-down or plasticized; cellulose acetate and cellulose acetate-butyrate in waste or scrap form, and in flake and powder form, not plasticized; carbon tetrachloride; methyl-ethyl ketone; ethyl ether; organo-fluorine compounds; ethylene diamine.

Also, aluminum sulfate; aluminum compounds; calcium hypochlorite (high-test bleaching powder, 70 percent chlorine); calcium carbide; calcium chloride; bromine, bromides and bromates; iodine, iodines and iodates; potassium bichromate and chromate; potassium hydroxide or caustic potash; boric acids and compounds (including borate esters and other borin compounds); sodium silicate or water glass; sodium carbonate, calcined (soda ash, not causticized); soda ash, causticized; sodium bicarbonate or baking soda; sodium bichromate or chromate; sodium cyanide; sodium triphosphate; sodium phosphate; sodium hydrosulfite; sodium sulfate; other sodium compounds; ammonium nitrate, except fertilizer; ammonium compounds, except fertilizer; ammonia, anhydrous and aqua, except as fertilizer; chlorine; hydrogen peroxide; gases, compressed, liquefied and solidified; and metal salts of organic compounds (except paint and varnish driers).

Chemicals and related products make up approximately three percent of the total traffic moving by barge and the volume is growing. In addition to the specific chemicals listed as now being transported others will come to water movement in the future.

Deck Barges

Deck barges serve a variety of purposes. Machinery, vehicles and heavy equipment can be moved aboard such vessels as can most any type cargo that can be tied down and which does not require protection from the elements. A great number of these vessels are used by the construction industry as work platforms and for moving and storing odds and ends of equipment and supplies. Dredging companies maintain fleets of these barges, with cargo boxes enclosing most of the deck area, to carry dredged materials such as sand, gravel, stone and shells to local markets. The logging industry also uses such barges to good advantage.

The deck barge is a simple box hull, generally with a heavy plated, well supported deck. The high combined center of gravity of the deck cargo and the hull can have an adverse effect on stability of this type of barge so that careful consideration must be given to hull size.

Generally they range in capacity from 350 tons to more than 1,500 tons. The most common sizes are 110 feet long by 26 feet wide; 130 feet long by 30 feet wide; and 195 feet long by 35 feet wide.

Miscellaneous Barges

A common sight in major coastal harbors are carfloats, a type of deck barge equipped with tracks to move 10, 20 or more railroad cars from one rail head to another or to shipside for transferring loads.

▲ A cylindrical tank is fitted into a barge to serve the chemical industry.

Grain is transferred directly from barge to truck.
▼

Rail car barge ferries provide regular service between Seattle, Washington and Whittier, Alaska. ►

Recently rail car barge ferries have been put in service between West Coast ports and Alaska, moving 30 or more cars.

Special barge types include dump scows with bottom doors for deep water use, side doors for shallow water use, and a capsizing type; self-unloading barges for cement and grain, and derrick and crane barges with lifting capacity up to 800 tons.

7 The Men Aboard

Skill, experience and a feel of the river are required to pilot a tow, some as long as the greatest ocean liners, through the inland waterways.

The river and canal towboat captains—and their crews—have these qualifications.

They must pilot their multi-unit vessels through narrow and sometimes

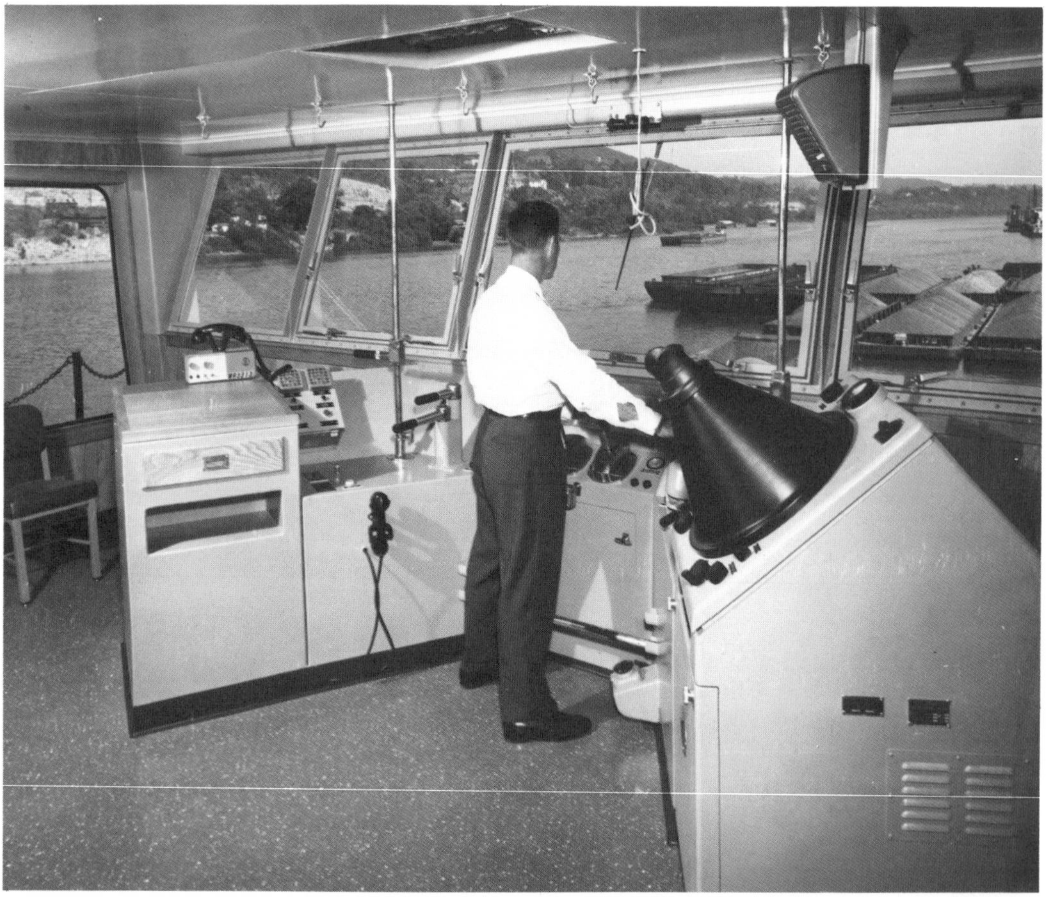

▲ This is a pilot of a modern towboat at work. He has at hand hydraulic steering controls, engine room controls, automatic pilot, radar, compass, depth indicator, swing indicator, searchlights, both long-range and short-range radio, intercom system and a public address system.

winding channels, between bridge piers with only inches to spare, and into and out of lock chambers where clearance again is often a matter of inches.

Their skills are tested when tows meet and pass for in these situations danger lurks in every movement of men and vessels.

But the men who pilot the towboats are equal to their task. Not only are they skilled in handling the towboats' sensitive controls with exactness but they literally carry in their minds a map of the river.

The barge and towing vessel industry has an outstanding personnel safety record. It is a living tribute to the skills of management, the captains, the pilots, and the crew of the towboats.

About 80,000 persons are employed aboard the vessels engaged in inland water transportation.

The size of a vessel's crew is determined by a number of factors, such as the size and power of the boat, the degree of its automation, the size of the tow (number of barges) which it is handling, and the waterway on which it is operating.

Vessel employees in line-haul operations work a 12-hour day, spending six hours on watch and six hours off, seven days per week, usually from the time the boat leaves its home port until it returns. There are instances, however, when crew changes are made en route. In general practice, the number of days crewmen work before they are given

▲ The engineer's room on a diesel towboat contains all the instrumentation and controls for proper operation of the main engines.

Bagged sugar is lifted from the hold of a barge and transferred to a truck for further shipment in a coordinated movement. ▼

▲ Deckhand securing safety line between two barges.

time off is determined by operating requirements. Crews normally work an 84-hour week. Vessel employees receive from one-third day off to a full day off at regular pay for each day worked. This practice is necessary to keep the boats in operation over long reaches of waterways where regularly scheduled crew replacements would be impractical.

Living conditions are recognized as important to operating efficiency. Four full meals are served every day. Laundry service is provided. Crew quarters are usually set apart from the noisier parts of the vessels, and in some cases are soundproofed. Working conditions aboard river boats have improved immeasurably in recent years. Many crews now enjoy the advantages of air-conditioning. Television and other recreational activities are provided aboard most boats.

Modern labor saving equipment with safety features for the protection of the crew have also made the work easier than in the era of the steamboat when the crew toiled endless hours at back-breaking work.

Wages in the industry have shown a steady increase. Actual pay varies for a

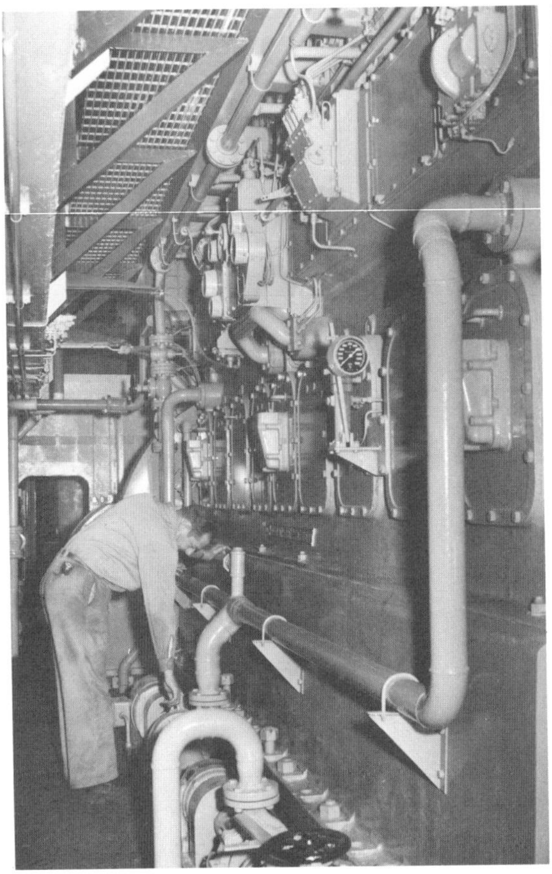

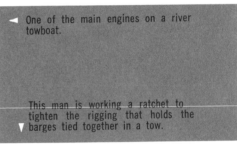

◄ One of the main engines on a river towboat.

This man is working a ratchet to tighten the rigging that holds the barges tied together in a tow. ▼

variety of reasons. Some lines are unionized, others are not. Legislation passed by the Congress in 1972 requires the licensing of pilothouse personnel aboard certain vessels.

Employment in the barge and towing vessel industry is stable. It is demanding in many ways, advancement is usually made through the ranks. Several universities and colleges are showing an interest in training men for careers in waterways transportation. These programs should provide more trained personnel in the years ahead.

The 80,000 employees working aboard the shallow-draft water carrier fleet provide three or four crews for each vessel because of the nature of the working schedules. Operating on a six-hour-on and six-hour-off schedule requires that two working crews be aboard the vessel at all times with a third and sometimes a fourth crew ashore for relief.

In 1961, towing vessel employees were brought under provisions of the Fair Labor Standards Act for purposes of minimum wages but are still exempted from the provisions of maximum hours and overtime.

The job of the crew begins with the make-up of the tow, except in the case of the integrated tow in which the barges are specially built to form a single unit and are not broken up. In the case of some line-haul operations, the tows are made up prior to the towboat's arrival.

In the make-up of a general river tow, putting together barges of all types and sizes requires time, energy and skill.

▲ Four meals a day and coffee around-the-clock come out of the galley of a towing vessel.

▲ Steel pipe being loaded into an open hopper barge.

▲ The tow is snubbed against the lock wall to hold it steady as the water in the chamber rises or falls during a lockage.

▲ A rail carfloat is tied to a tug for transfer.

◄ Valves and hose connections are checked in a tank barge loading operation.

Because the boat handling a general tow will pick up or set out loaded and unloaded barges at many points along its route, the positioning of any barge for discharge en route is very important.

A loudspeaker system or walkie-talkie radio keeps the captain in the pilothouse in direct communication with the mate out on the tow. The towboat has to be maneuvered without hitch in the difficult and frequently hazardous process of backing, turning and swinging barges in order to make up a tow as quickly as possible.

With rigging of wire cables and ropes the deckhands join the barges into an end-to-end formation. The job is eased by stationary ratchets and winches on each end of the barges, holding down the amount of loose rigging that must be carried. A good deckhand exercises as much dexterity as a cowboy in handling the heavy lines used to lash the barges.

Make-up of the tow in many operations is handled by a special crew using a small workboat. In many of the major ports this work—as well as the break-up of tows and distribution of barges to loading and unloading docks—is handled by harbor fleet operators. Thus line-haul towboats can arrive in port, cut loose from their tow of barges, take on another tow which is already made up and be on their way again in an hour or two.

Once under way with instructions from company traffic officials, the captain puts to work the latest technological advances that have eased the burden of river navigation. Neither night, fog nor snow delays him. With fingertip control of immense power, he can move thousands of tons of cargo safely and efficiently over thousands of miles of water highway.

8 The Channels

The United States has 25,543 miles of usable navigable inland channels, exclusive of the Great Lakes. A nine-foot operating depth is standard for these inland channels. Of the 25,543 miles, a total of 15,675 miles have a depth of nine feet or more. The remaining 9,868 miles is under nine-foot depth. Except for the 522-mile New York State Barge Canal all of these waterways are Federal projects.

With the exception of the Upper Mississippi Waterway, the Missouri River and the New York State Barge Canal, all the inland channels are open to navigation the year 'round. Icing conditions close the three waterways named for about four months of the year—December through March. At times, ice forms on the Illinois Waterway, the Mississippi above St. Louis, and on the Ohio River, but seldom impedes navigation for any length of time.

With two notable exceptions the channels are slack water routes which have been improved for navigation by the construction of systems of locks and dams. The Mississippi is open river for 1,000 miles south of St. Louis. The Missouri is open river. Yet the two present a striking difference. The Mississippi is a wide, deep, commodious river. The Missouri has a restricted seven-foot depth. Both the Atlantic and Gulf Intracoastal Waterways are largely open channels, although both have some locks and both have reaches that are exposed to tidal currents and winds.

Most of the current waterway construction projects involve work to widen or deepen channels or to modernize channels by the construction of higher dams and larger locks.

The redevelopment of the Ohio River, for instance, is under way. The river was canalized in 1929 by a system of 52 locks and dams. The new canalization project which was started in 1955 will replace the present lock and dam system with 19 new high lift locks with lock chambers 110 feet wide by 1,200 feet long. The present chambers are 110 feet by 600 feet.

Modernization of the Warrior-Tombigbee River System, initiated in 1937 to replace the original 17 locks and dams with six new locks and dams, is scheduled to be completed in 1975 when the new high lift Bankhead Lock goes into operation. Replacement of the William Bacon Oliver lock, the first of the modernization program, with a standard 110-foot by 600-foot lock and channel cutoffs and enlargement is under study.

The plan of improvement on the Illinois Waterway provides for duplicate new locks, 110 feet wide by 1,200 feet long to supplement the existing shorter locks at the present lock sites.

Construction of the 253-mile Tennessee-Tombigbee Waterway got underway in December 1972. This $386.6 million project will provide a shorter, more direct connecting waterway between the Tennessee River and the Gulf of Mexico at Mobile, Alabama.

Widening and deepening of the Gulf Intracoastal Waterway, St. Marks to Tampa Bay, Florida, to 12 feet by 150 feet has been authorized. However, an economic re-study is now underway to recompute the benefit cost ratio that was based on existence of the Cross-Florida Barge Canal, construction of which is now halted.

Construction on the Cross-Florida Barge Canal was stopped in January 1971. At that time the project was approximately 40 percent complete. President Nixon issued an order on January 19, 1971 halting the project. This action was recommended by the Council on Environmental Quality and by various environmental groups. The planned Canal would have provided a 185-mile, 12 foot deep waterway with five single lift locks 84 feet by 600 feet, linking the Atlantic Intracoastal Waterway at Jacksonville, Florida to the Gulf of Mexico through the Withlacoochee River valley 95 miles north of Tampa on the west coast of Florida.

The navigation feature of the McClellan-Kerr Arkansas River Navigation System consists of 17 locks and dams which are in operation and provide a nine foot navigational channel from the Mississippi River to Catoosa, near Tulsa, Oklahoma. When navigation was opened to Tulsa (Catoosa) in 1970 it provided additional 450 miles of navigation channel.

Work is continuing on the nine-foot channel on the Missouri River. The entire project from Sioux City, Iowa to the mouth will stabilize the banks of the river and provide a navigation channel for waterborne commerce.

The Alabama River channel improvement extending from its mouth to Montgomery, Alabama, is basically complete. Additional work to stabilize a nine foot channel is underway.

The Chattahoochee River has been canalized and opened to navigation as far north as Columbus, Georgia, and studies are under way on extending this navigation system to Atlanta.

Some portions of these projects are included in the authorized navigable channel system; others represent new projects or additions to presently authorized projects.

Without the modern dredge the inland waterways system of the United States would neither exist nor function. Dredging is necessary to achieve uniform channel depth in the initial construction of practically every commercial waterway. Dredging is a part of the construction of locks and dams.

Completion of the initial construction phase of a waterway does not end the need for dredging. Normal silting builds up shoals and bars. Vessel movements themselves sometimes shift channel bottoms and contour lines. High water flows increase silting and cause shoals and bars to build up. To maintain the navigation channels, supervised dredging is necessary on most waterways. It is done under direction of the Corps of Engineers primarily by private contractors.

All the inland water routes are Federal navigation projects with the exception of the New York State Barge Canal which was built by the state and which is state owned and operated. The New York State Legislature in 1959 passed a constitutional amendment authorizing transfer of the Barge Canal to the Federal Government. Following a four-year study a Joint Legislative Committee of the State of New York recommended that the state retain control of the Barge Canal. Shipping interests generally favor the proposed transfer and are continuing to fight for it. They believe the transfer would result in much-needed improvements and provide a modern, efficient commercial navigation artery.

No charges of any kind are made for use of the inland navigation channels either for commercial transportation or for use by pleasure craft. Efforts have been made from time to time by various interests to have a toll or user charge put in effect, but none of these efforts has succeeded.

Water carriers and allied interests oppose the levying of any tolls, toll-equivalent taxes or user charges. The position is based on the fact that the nation's water courses have been improved as Federal projects for navigation as a means of general economic development which would be retarded by the imposition of such charges, and on the theory that tolls would retard and limit the distribution of such benefits as are inherent in improved navigation channels.

9 SAFETY

Safety is a matter of continuing and vital concern to the barge and towing industry—concern for the welfare of the men and women employed aboard the tows, concern for the general public in the areas where transportation is performed, concern for the safety and integrity of the cargoes carried, and concern for efficient service to shippers.

The industry has achieved an outstanding safety record. Nevertheless, constant vigilance is necessary to improve this record. As a measure of the concern and accomplishment for safety, records show that in the performance of inland waterborne freight service the total fatality per billion ton-miles in 1968 was 0.54. To appreciate this figure, it is necessary to note that for rail freight service the total fatality per billion ton-miles in 1968 was 2.5; and for motor carrier freight service the total fatality per billion ton-miles was 10.8 the same year.

Even though the barge and towing industry has a remarkable safety record, the industry believes that it can be improved and will be improved by working in concert and in cooperation with the agencies which have responsibility in this field, particularly the United States Coast Guard.

In the area of safety, the industry is guided and governed by some of the most highly developed regulatory controls in existence to safeguard the movements of oil and the so-called dangerous cargoes. The marine industry, in cooperation with the United States Coast Guard, has been formulating and updating such regulations for many years; and will continue to improve the regulations and hopefully improve the safety of operations and insure the public safety.

An excellent example of industry-Coast Guard cooperative efforts in developing regulations involved the agency's proposed rules designed to minimize oil pollution from vessels and loading facilities. Authority for the rules is contained in the Water Quality Improvement Act of 1970. The industry worked closely with the Coast Guard in the development of the regulations and several of its recommendations and suggestions were accepted by that agency.

The industry, in the interest of safety, supported legislation to license the men in charge of navigating towing vessels, which became Public Law 92-339, and to unify and consolidate the Rules of the Road. The industry also supported legislation to require bridge-to-bridge radiotelephones on towing vessels which became Public Law 92-63.

The American Waterways Operators, Inc. maintains an active, standing safety committee of its members which is concerned with all aspects of vessel personnel, environmental and navigational safety. This committee has produced a Basic Safety Manual for the industry and on a monthly basis distributes a safety poster devoted to a specific inland waterway safety topic. Safety Committee members and AWO staff personnel also actively participate in the Marine Section activities of the National Safety Council and several state and local safety associations as well. These activities include responsibility for the Inland Waterways Section program at the National Safety Congress held annually in Chicago. AWO and the National Safety Council also jointly sponsor an industry-wide, annual towing safety contest.

10 OCEAN BARGING

One of the most dramatic developments in the barge and towing industry in recent years has been the increase in use of ocean barging and its emergence as an important factor in our total transportation system. Recent developments in technology and the realization by operators and shippers of its economic potential indicate even greater usage of ocean barging in the future.

Ranging in size up to 35,000 deadweight tons, the big vessels transport oil and dry bulk cargo along the Atlantic and Gulf Coasts and into the Caribbean, and along the Pacific Coast to Alaska and Hawaii. Propulsion is provided by tugboats which either pull the barges by means of a towline or push them.

Ocean tugboats range in length from 100 feet to over 150 feet and from 1,500 horsepower to over 9,000 horsepower. The average, however, is 125 feet long and is powered by an engine of from 1,500 to 3,200 horsepower. Draft ranges from 10 feet to over 20 feet.

Most of these vessels are open hopper, covered dry cargo, deck and tank barges, all of which are entirely of welded steel construction.

Several categories of barges are employed as single operating units. Basically, these are of 7,500 to 12,000 deadweight tons and are towed by tugs of 2,000 to 3,200 horsepower. They are primarily engaged in the supply of fuels to population centers, nearby refineries or transshipment points. A typical barge in this service has a length of 350 feet, breadth of 66 feet, and a draft of 26 feet. Such a barge is propelled by a tug measuring 110 feet in length, breadth 25 feet and a draft of 17 feet, and is of 3,200 horsepower.

Another range of barge is in the 12,000 to 20,000 deadweight ton group which includes lumber products carriers, cement barges and the petroleum vessels. A typical barge of this size is 400 feet long by 68 feet wide, which is towed by a tug of approximately 4,000 horsepower whose dimensions might be 120 feet long, 35 feet wide with a draft of 19 feet.

The next group of barges include vessels up to 35,000 deadweight tons whose dimensions are approximately 550 feet by 85 feet by 42 feet. Vessels in this very large category have only been tanker types thus far and with them have come the integrated tug-barge units, an American development that appears to have promise. At the present time, it is estimated that more than 54,000,000 tons of cargo move annually in oceangoing barges.

The primary interest in oceangoing barging today stems mainly from the economies afforded. For example, a tugboat and barge unit require substan-

Giant oceangoing tug and barge hauling petroleum products from a refinery near Philadelphia to Boston and Portland, Maine. Discharge time for the 31,000 ton barge is 14.5 hours for 255,000 barrels.

Approximately 5,670,000 gallons of petroleum products enroute to Tampa, Florida from a New Orleans refinery.

tially less men than a ship of the same deadweight ton capacity. On the West Coast an eight- to 12-14 man crew is required for barge operations between Alaska, Washington, Oregon and California. The crew of a 4,000 to 12,000 deadweight ton ship plying the same route will range from 25 to 45 men.

The World War II vintage T-2 tanker, a self-contained ship which ocean barges are replacing, requires a crew of approximately 34 men. A 30,000 ton barge, carrying twice the payload of the T-2 tanker, is propelled by a tug whose crew ranges from nine to 15 men, depending on the size of the tugboat and the job to be performed.

Oceangoing barges carrying up to 12,500 tons of general cargo are also in service with the same kind of economies.

Another important factor favoring ocean barging is construction cost. The capital required for construction of a tugboat and barge combination is substantially lower than for a standard oceangoing vessel built in the United States.

A number of revolutionary innovations have occurred in ocean barging in recent years. The Seabee and LASH systems marry barges and oceangoing vessels into a new transportation system. These systems are turning inland ports into seaports in addition to penetrating deep into the heartland of Europe.

Specially built ships are used to transport the barges in these two systems in oceangoing commerce. The barges are taken from the ship and moved over inland waterway channels as barges for loading and unloading at origin and destination points.

The LASH system, employing barges of about 400 gross ton capacity, is already in operation. Barges of about 750

◄ A 12,000-ton limestone barge on a weekly run between Astoria and Lake Oswego, Oregon.

Two thousand horsepower tug leaving Puget Sound for Cook Inlet, Alaska with tanden two consisting of a 260 foot barge carrying 2,700 tons of pipe and a pipe laying barge. ▼

▼ Oceangoing tugboat with two seagoing barges in tow crossing the Gulf of Mexico.

LASH System, another revolutionary new concept in intermodal sea transportation. The mother ship has an overall length of 820 feet and a dry cargo capacity of 20,263 long tons of 1,435,500 cubic feet of cargo in 73 LASH lighters. Or, 1,650,816 cubic feet in 1,498 standard 20 foot containers.

Seabee now in service between U. S.-Gulf United Kingdom-Western Europe ports. Almost three city blocks in length, the 875 foot barge carrier can transport 38 fully loaded barges or 1,800 containers or vehicles.

ton capacity (one half the size of standard river barges) which make up the Seabee system are also in operation. These two systems brought new types of service to interior points now served only by conventional towing and barge service.

Another type of innovative service in operations on the inland waterways, primarily the Mississippi River, are the Mini-Ships. This system employs self-propelled vessels of approximately 3,100 deadweight tons for the transportation of all types of commodities. The vessels are of Greek registry and carry an eight man crew. North of Baton Rouge, Louisiana the draft limitations prevent the Mini-Ships from fully utilizing their cubic capacities.

One of the interesting developments in ocean barging occurred in 1963 with the introduction of a coastal rail-car barge for operation between Seattle and Alaska. This service, which provides a direct rail-water link between Seattle and Alaska, uses mammoth ocean barges to transport up to 64 loaded rail cars with all kinds of commodities from the continental United States to Alaska.

One oceangoing integrated tug and barge unit is expected to be the world's largest such unit when it is completed late in 1973. The unit includes a catamaran-type tug powered by two diesel engines with 7,000 horsepower each for a total of 14,000 horsepower.

The combination unit will be about 629 feet in length over all, and have a beam of 95 feet. It will have a cargo tank capacity of about 320,000 barrels. Marine engineers report it will be able to move at about 14.6 knots.

The catamaran tug-barge unit locks together with rigid connection between tug and barge. It is detachable in a matter of minutes. The stern of the barge is designed to fit and lock between the twin hulls of the catamaran tug.

Still another recent development is the construction of the first oceangoing barge in the United States to carry liquefied natural gas to terminals on the East Coast. This self-unloading barge has been engineered to protect and carry its supercold energy at a temperature of near minus 260 degrees Fahrenheit in four heavy aluminum cylindrical tanks. Through the use of electrically-driven pumps installed in each of the four tanks, the barge's capacity of 32,000

Oceangoing integrated tug and barge unit which is expected to be the world's largest such unit when completed. The unit includes a catamaran-type tug powered by two diesel engines with 7,000 horsepower each for a total of 14,000 horsepower. The combination until will be about 629 feet in length all over, and have a beam of 95 feet. It will have a cargo tank capacity of about 320,000 barrels.

▲ Ocean tugboats moving component parts for a gas freezing plant from New Orleans to Venezuela.

barrels of liquid methane is expected to be discharged at the rate of 7,000 gallons per minute.

In recent years serious research and experimentation has been going on throughout the maritime industry to develop an improved method of connecting oceangoing tugboats and barges. Such research and experimenting, with its promise of lower costs for construction and operation as well as greater maneuverability, seaworthiness and safety, has generated keen interest and optimism among barge operators, shipowners and shippers.

To date there have been several different designs for the linkage of large tow-barge combinations. Some of them already are in service, using carefully matched surfaces and mechanical system of holding the separable bodies tighly together, thus replacing the traditional winches and wires which hold the tug's forebody into the barge's notched stern.

These latest advances in oceangoing tug-barge technology bring forth an entirely new concept in deep-sea shipping which could have a dramatic impact.

11 Locks and Dams

Sizes of the lock chambers which pass vessels from one level of water to the other in canalized streams have tended to dictate standardization of the dimensions of vessels using the inland channels.

The Corps of Engineers of the United States Army, the agency charged under Congressional authority with the responsibility to construct, develop, maintain, and operate the Federally authorized navigation channels, says in a booklet, entitled "Engineering and Design—Navigation Locks," that "Lock design and barge design have influenced each other to such an extent that the size of each are now in general harmony." The Corps has established the following standard usable lock dimensions for the waterways of the United States:

- Lock width of 66 feet with length of either 400 feet or 600 feet
- Lock width of 84 feet with length of 600 feet, 800 feet, or 1,200 feet
- Lock width of 110 feet with length of 600 feet, 800 feet, or 1,200 feet.

These standard dimensions were established in 1959. Many locks built prior to that time or which were under construction at that time do not conform to the standards.

Locks on the Columbia-Snake River System are 86 feet wide by 675 feet long on the major portion of the waterway and either 86 feet by 500 feet or 86 feet by 360 feet on smaller tributary streams.

The section of this booklet dealing with individual waterways gives the prevailing sizes of the locks on the various waterways.

Twenty-four standard 175-foot-by-26-foot barges make up a tow four abreast and six long, less one barge out for the

A deckhand stands aboard one of the barges in a petroleum tow as it moves into a lock on the Upper Mississippi River. Note the line at his feet that he will use to hold the tow in place along the lock wall as the water raises the barges and towboat.

towboat, for passage through a lock chamber 110 feet wide by 1,200 feet long; or four abreast and three long with one barge out for the towboat to pass through a lock chamber 110 feet by 600 feet. Barges of standard length of 195 feet by 35 feet wide can be made up three abreast and six long and three abreast and three long for passage respectively through a standard size lock chamber of 110 feet wide by 1,200 feet long or 110 feet wide by 600 feet long.

Lock chambers of adequate size to accommodate the type of tows that operate on a waterway are important to the economics of barge transportation. The average lock is designed to accommodate the passage of vessels in a 20 to 30 minute operation. Single tows which are too large to pass through a lock in a single operation require double lockage. Breakup and reassembly of the tow together with the two lockage operations takes about an hour and a half. Since operating costs of a towboat average from $50 to $100 per hour, double lockages impose a cost penalty to operators and added costs to shippers.

Dams are essential to maintain reasonably constant water depth for year-around navigation on most rivers. Winter cold, spring flooding, summer

WHY NAVIGATION LOCKS AND DAMS ARE NECESSARY

Winter cold, spring flooding, and summer heat produce wide variations in the depth of a natural river. A series of dams in such a river helps to maintain a more constant depth to permit year around use by river traffic. Navigation locks are the means by which river traffic is passed from one level to another created by the dam. This action can either be up or down. Follow the towboat in the diagrams as it passes from the upper level to the lower level.

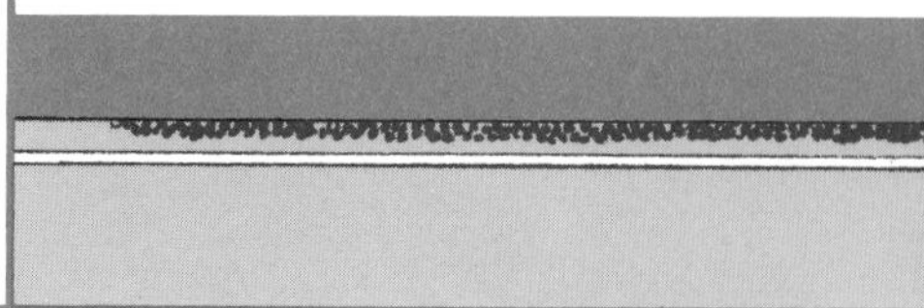

HOW NAVIGATION LOCKS OPERATE

Diagram #1

The lower gates (D) are closed; the drain valve (B) is closed; the filling valve (A) is open allowing the lock chamber to fill to the upper level; and the upper gates (C) have been opened allowing the towboat to enter the lock chamber.

Diagram #2

Now the towboat is in the lock chamber; the upper gates (C) are closed; the filling valve (A) is closed; the drain valve (B) is open allowing water to drain out into the lower level. The towboat is lowered as the water level lowers.

Diagram #3

When the water level reaches the lower level, the lower gates (D) are opened allowing the towboat to leave the lock chamber and proceed on down the river to the next lock and dam where it will go through the same procedure.

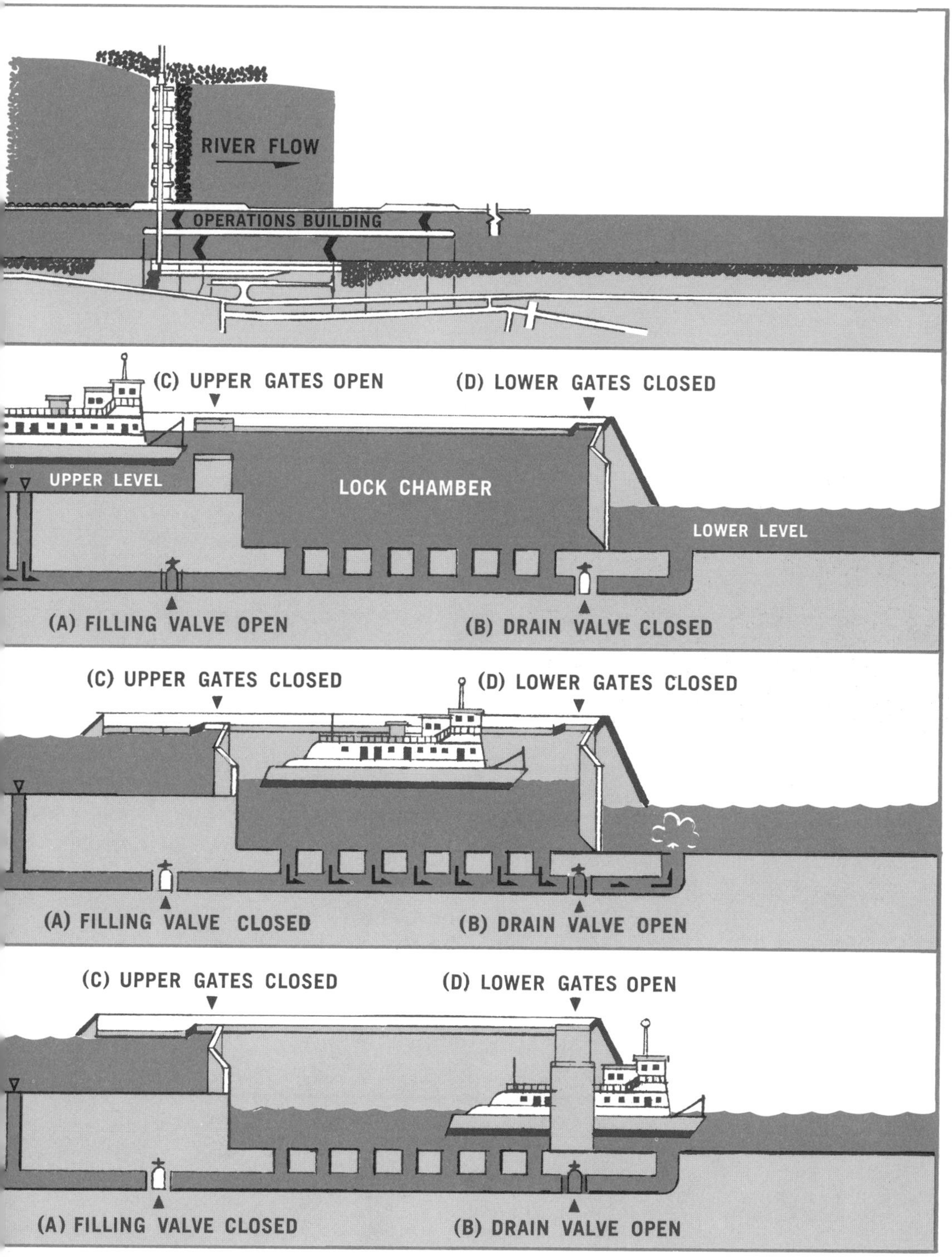
RIVER FLOW
OPERATIONS BUILDING
(C) UPPER GATES OPEN
(D) LOWER GATES CLOSED
UPPER LEVEL
LOCK CHAMBER
LOWER LEVEL
(A) FILLING VALVE OPEN
(B) DRAIN VALVE CLOSED
(C) UPPER GATES CLOSED
(D) LOWER GATES CLOSED
(A) FILLING VALVE CLOSED
(B) DRAIN VALVE OPEN
(C) UPPER GATES CLOSED
(D) LOWER GATES OPEN
(A) FILLING VALVE CLOSED
(B) DRAIN VALVE OPEN

◄ This is Pickwick Lock and Dam on the Tennessee River at Savannah, Tennessee. The dam creates a still water navigation pool 52.7 miles long between Savannah and Florence, Alabama. This is an example of multiple-purpose development and use of water resources with hydroelectric power production as an integral part. Hand-in-hand with power production and navigation go enhancement of load values, recreation facilities, industrial production opportunities, and flood control.

◄ This tow of 15 barges is too big to go through Lock 11 on the Mississippi River above Dubuque, Iowa, in a single lockage operation. Nine barges have been locked through first. Now the other six barges and the towboat are going through the lock. The tow will be remade and proceed on its journey to deliver 22,000 tons of coal.

heat, and drought periods produce wide variations in water depths of a natural river. A series of dams which create pools of water in a river overcomes this problem and provides a stable channel for navigation. These dams do more than just provide adequate depth of water and relatively calm water to support a system of commercial navigation. In many instances they provide a substantial measure of flood control. They provide stable water supplies to support industrial manufacturing processes. Such water supplies are often beneficial to agricultural communities for irrigation purposes and to municipalities for their varied uses. Many navigation projects are created by the construction of multiple purpose dams which include the generation of hydroelectric energy in addition to all the other water resource development benefits. The pools created by dams afford ideal opportunities for pleasure boating and other water-related recreation activities. All of these related water resources development assets which accompany the construction of navigation dams enhance the value of lands adjacent to the waterways, thus creating another source of added economic wealth.

▲ The bow steering unit concept is not new; its modern application and use is. It adds steering control at the head of the tow; is especially helpful for guidance around bends; increases efficiency considerably. Some have thrust power as well as steering power. This one is radio controlled from the towboat's pilot house

12 Ports and Terminals

River and canal transportation make ports of some of the major inland cities of the United States. Their port activity creates additional economic wealth through added employment and added purchasing power.

The growth and expansion of inland waterways transportation has resulted in the construction of many new and modern terminals for the handling of freight to and from barges, and for exchange of freight between water carriers and other modes of transportation at ports throughout the United States. These port facilities represent substantial investments on the part of water carriers and other private interests, as well as some public bodies created for this purpose. Much waterfront land has been developed in these port cities, both for port facilities and for waterside-located production facilities. Property values have been increased and new sources of municipal tax revenue have become available.

Inland waterways transportation helps to create and sustain a variety of port services such as warehousing, boat supplies, dry dock and boat repairing, bunkering, marine insurance, banking, fleeting operations, and harbor towing. All of these services add to the business development of the port cities in which they are located and operated.

Coastal ports that are connected with the commercial river and canal channels are fed by inland commerce in addition to oceangoing commerce. This inland commerce has been stimulated by the nation's need for imports as well as by the growth of exports.

Dependence of cities upon inland waterways transportation is particularly apparent, for example, in the case of the port of New Orleans on the Mississippi River where approximately half of the total commerce which utilizes its extensive facilities is inland waterway traffic.

The major portion of terminaling work to service inland water carrier operations is carried out through facilities provided by shippers and receivers.

The growth of barge transportation has spurred interest in public terminals and there has been substantial increase in this field of service. Many are operated in busy port areas by private interests. States, counties, municipalities, and port districts are recognizing the economic advantages of adequate terminal facilities. Public terminals generally provide docks, wharves, the necessary loading and unloading equipment, warehouses, tank farms, and open storage for the types of commodities that move by barge. In seaport areas, terminals generally serve both shallow-draft inland vessel operations and deep-draft oceangoing vessel operations. Along the inland waterways, docks are built at proper elevations to insure that the rise and fall of the river will not affect operations.

Privately operated terminals, of course, are designed and operated to meet the particular needs of the shipper or receiver.

Modern terminals are highly mechanized installations designed to permit fast loading and delivery, thereby eliminating unnecessary delays and speeding up vessel turnaround time. Mechanization, is, of course, readily applicable to the handling of bulk-loading cargoes at low cost. Terminaling costs on non-bulk freight are necessarily higher because of the labor involved. Inland water lines and terminal operators work closely together to hold freight handling costs at a minimum.

The equipment available for proper handling of the type cargo that moves by barge is extensive. It includes various sizes of cranes, many types of gear for movement of cargo by the crane, fork trucks of various sizes to handle the various weights of unit loads, clam shells and hoppers for bulk commodity handling, conveyors, two-wheel and four-wheel trucks, power mules to move trucks in tandem style, pallets, highlifts and a multitude of other types of equipment and gear.

Most public terminals along the inland waterways have railroad and highway connections which permit the direct interchange of freight between barges and other floating equipment on the one hand, and railroad cars and motor trucks on the other.

The modern combination river, rail, and truck terminals have warehouse and open storage facilities available to the users of inland water transportation. Shipment in larger quantities with storage available in or near the desired markets may improve delivery service or earn more economical freight rates on volume shipments. Terminal operators provide facilities for inspection of goods and other services which enable shippers not only to meet competition but to expand the market areas for their products.

13 The Public Interest

The contribution of improved inland waterways to the general welfare is nationwide in scope. The national character of the public interest in waterways is clear from the national spread of benefits as a return on the investment for improvements for navigation and other associated purposes. The benefits are broad in scope and nature as well as in distribution and sharing. These benefits include economic development through better transportation services.

A number of agencies of the federal government therefore have extensive responsibilities in connection with water transportation. The Army Corps of Engineers has responsibility for the physical plant, that is, for planning, design, construction, operation and maintenance of the locks and dams, the channels, and the bank protective works. The United States Coast Guard has responsibilities on the inland waterways similar to its duties along the coasts and at sea—navigation aids and safety of life. Other aspects of the welfare of the inland water transportation industry that arise from its place in the national transportation system—rail, highway, air, pipeline, and water—include the regulatory responsibility of the Interstate Commerce Commission. The Federal Communications Commission allocates the channels which the industry uses for radio and radiotelephone communications.

14 The Environment

Pollution control, protection and enhancement of the environment, and maintenance of the ecological balance have long been of major interest to the barge and towing industry. The industry adopted the position several years ago that it favored, supported, and would aggressively work to control that portion of pollution which the industry contributes to the navigable waters, even though authorities agree that such contribution is negligible.

This interest and concern over clean water caused the industry, starting in the 1950's, to begin analyzing operations to determine measures that it might take to alleviate that portion of the pollution of navigable waters created by the industry. Through the years, these efforts have been refined to create a better pattern of environmental management on the navigable waters.

In doing so, the industry has worked closely with the Congress, departments of the government, and agencies having pollution control responsibilities.

The industry's broad objective is to achieve a balanced program consistent with the needs for pollution control and enhancement of the environment which will not unduly restrain the development of transport resources nor place undue burdens upon interstate commerce.

The effort is complicated by the widespread diffusion of pollution control responsibilities within the Federal establishment and by a proliferation of state laws with different standards and requirements.

The basic Federal water pollution law affecting vessels is the Federal Water Pollution Control Act to which the industry has made significant contributions. The basic enforcement authority for vessel water pollution under the Act is the primary responsibility of the Coast Guard.

The Federal act was substantially amended in 1970 and again in 1972. These latest amendments imposed upon vessels traversing United States navigable waters, water pollution control laws which are among the most stringent and rigidly enforced laws of any nation in the world.

The Federal Water Pollution Control Act contains provisions which prohibit vessel sewage discharges. Discharge standards established by the Environmental Protection Agency and enforcement regulations promulgated by the Coast Guard under the act require holding tanks to contain sewage discharges on board all new vessels by 1975 and such a modification on all existing vessels by 1982. The holding tanks will be discharged into shoreside facilities where the sewage will be treated.

Under the Federal act anyone found guilty of deliberately discharging oil or certain other substances is subject to unlimited financial liability for cleanup costs.

The liability of a vessel for cleanup costs for negligently or accidentally discharging oil or responsible for another vessel accidentally discharging oil is $100 per gross ton of the vessel or $14,000,000, whichever is less.

The penalty for the accidental discharge is payable to the Federal government to cover the cost of Federal cleanup if the discharger himself fails to clean up the spill. In 1972, an amendment was added to the bill establishing an identical cleanup penalty to cover accidental discharges of substances other than oil which are both toxic and removable from water.

Also added in 1972 was a fine up to $50,000 for accidental discharges of substances which are both toxic and unremovable from water. On October 18, 1974, two years to the date after enactment of the 1972 amendments to the law, the maximum fine that can be imposed for unremovable substances will automatically escalate from $50,000 to $5,000,000.

The industry has a very deep concern with laws which impose fines so high that they are punitive. Penalties in the form of fines of such a magnitude, which are not for specific cleanup costs or actual damages but for civil or criminal violations, are not insurable.

To insure the continuance of waterborne transportation of petroleum products, and other substances removable from water, the Congress included in the Federal Water Pollution Control Act insurable limitations on the amount of financial liability for which a vessel could be held responsible for cleanup costs—$100 per gross ton of the vessel or $14,000,000, whichever is less. This permits waterborne commerce of vitally needed petroleum and removable chemical substances to proceed under a commercially insurable risk with a guarantee to the Federal government that discharge cleanup costs are covered.

In addition the Federal act requires vessel owners to establish their evidence of financial responsibility for cleanup costs through one of several methods. Commercial marine insurance, mentioned above, is one of the most common methods. Failure to obtain a certificate of financial responsibility from the Federal Maritime Commission can subject a vessel owner or operator to a fine up to $10,000 plus his vessel may be denied entry or exit from a U. S. port until he is able to post a sufficient bond.

Other penalties under the Federal act provide for a civil fine up to $5,000 for any discharge from a vessel in addition to the penalties for cleaning up discharges. Also, failure to notify the Coast Guard immediately about the occurrence of a spill subjects anyone with such knowledge to a fine of up to $10,000. The purpose of this fine is to encourage the reporting of accidental discharges so that they can be cleaned up before they become too widespread.

The Federal Water Pollution Control Act also provides for a National Contingency Plan operated on a cooperative basis with the states and local port and harbor agencies. Its purpose is to provide an immediate cleanup response to any discharge. The failure to obey National Contingency Plan regulations or maritime navigation and safety law regulations used in conjunction with the Plan subjects any violators to a fine up to $10,000.

Another law used to impose penalties

for discharges is the Refuse Act of 1899 for which the Corps of Engineers has basic enforcement responsibilities. It provides for a penalty up to $2,500 and/or imprisonment for up to one year for any release of refuse (including petroleum products) into the navigable waters of the United States. Most often it is used to impose penalties on shore-based plants and vehicles, but it has been used on occasion for vessel discharges. The Federal Water Pollution Control Act also provides for a penalty up to $8,000,000 for discharges into U. S. navigable waters from offshore and onshore facilities (such as drilling rigs, manufacturing plants, storage tanks, and vehicles).

In addition to the Federal Water Pollution Control Act and the 1899 Refuse Act there are maritime safety and navigation laws of which the primary purpose is to protect life and property on the waterways, but which also have as an indirect purpose the prevention of pollution.

Among these are the Ports and Waterways Safety Act of 1972 which permits the Coast Guard to establish vessel traffic control systems in all United States ports and harbors. The more congested the port or harbor, or the more frequently it is subjected to bad weather problems, the more likely the Coast Guard will establish a vessel traffic system to prevent accidents and the resulting pollution. Systems are already underway in the ports of Seattle and San Francisco and planned for New Orleans, New York, Galveston, Houston, and on certain segments of the inland waterways.

A 1972 Act to license operators of towing vessels and create the new Coast Guard license category of "Operator" now permits the Coast Guard to establish qualifications and examinations under which towing vessel operators may be formally tested and licensed.

The Bridge-to-Bridge Radiotelephone Act of 1971 requires vessel personnel in the pilothouse to keep a listening-watch on a safety channel at all times while the vessel is underway so that they have full knowledge of the navigation intentions of all other vessels in their immediate vicinity.

Other Federal laws and regulations provide for the inspection of all tank vessels and licensing and manning requirements for the crew aboard such vessels to assure that they have the requisite knowledge, experience, and physical ability to operate the vessels safely and assure the safest possible transfer of petroleum and chemical cargoes from the vessels to storage facilities or other vessels.

As previously noted, in addition to a stringent Federal water pollution law, the industry is also subjected to a proliferation of state and local water pollution laws and regulations. Such laws are in effect in over 30 coastal states. In some cases they parallel the Federal statutes, overlap them in others, and in some instances they are more restrictive. In any sense these state laws are usually in conflict with one another as well as with the Federal law. Compliance by a vessel with the laws of one jurisdiction may only serve to bring it in violation of the laws of other adjacent jurisdictions.

The industry believes that laws and regulations that govern vessels moving in interstate commerce must comprise a uniform nationwide system. To provide otherwise severely limits a vessel's use and movement and results in operational inefficiencies that contribute to higher consumer costs for goods and water transportation without any concurrent improvement in environmental protection. The industry does not believe that state laws dealing with pollution control and waste from watercraft must be totally preempted or that state

Petroleum tow on the Mississippi

and administrative officers should be denied a role in the cleanup of discharges of oil and hazardous substances, but the industry believes that state laws and regulations should be compatible with the Federal system of regulation.

To facilitate the movement of waterborne commerce on its own behalf, on behalf of the shippers, and on behalf of the public which benefits from low-cost transportation, the industry has recommended first, that to the extent that provisions in state laws which impose liabilities in excess of amounts that are determined to be insurable, such provisions should be preempted. Otherwise the excessive and duplicative risk of liability under state law would stand as a harsh deterrent to the movement of vessels from state to state. The industry also believes that provisions in state laws which impose civil or criminal penalties, in addition to any provided under Federal law, should also be preempted. The industry further believes that there is a need to eliminate the overlap and conflict with Federal laws.

Secondly, the industry feels that one of the fundamental questions that needs to be decided within the Federal government itself is the centralization of responsibility. Federal agencies currently having maritime responsibilities are seeking to coordinate their work, insofar as possible, so as not to impose unnecessary burdens upon marine transportation. But such voluntary coordination within the Federal establishment by large departments is at best unwieldy. The administration of water pollution laws and regulations by a single Federal agency would be highly desirable.

In the absence of such single agency administration, the industry seeks a clear-cut delineation of the jurisdiction of water pollution control among the Environmental Protection Agency, the United States Coast Guard, the Army Corps of Engineers, and the Federal Maritime Commission, all of which now exercise certain responsibilities under the Federal water pollution control laws affecting vessels.

15 Joint Transportation Benefits

Each mode of transportation acts as an economic stimulator which redounds to the advantage of the other modes.

Barge transportation is particularly suited to this role because of its inherent ability to move at low cost the bulk-loading raw materials—as well as many finished and semi-finished products—for our production industries. Low cost delivery of raw materials determines and supports distribution patterns. Together these attributes of water transport stimulate existing industry and create opportunities for new business. And all forms of transportation become economic beneficiaries.

More than 50 percent of all domestic freight shipments and nearly 100 percent of all foreign trade cargoes require the services of more than one form of transportation. For instance, a large part of water-borne tonnage in the United States is either prehandled or rehandled by railroads.

Arteries of rail, air, and highway transport coincide with virtually every water navigation improvement or extension. Where the water traffic has the greatest density, there the rail, air, and highway commerce is generally heaviest. Where new general service river terminals are built the railroads have a wharf track.

Thus barge-to-rail, barge-to-truck, barge-to-air, barge-to-pipeline, and all the many other transportation combinations are vital to the commercial, industrial, and cultural development of the United States.

Yet, despite this, there is constant competitive strife in the transportation ranks which often causes serious harm to the public interest. The railroads are the most notable offenders in this regard, primarily through certain rate-making practices with respect to competitive traffic and through a steady stream of legislative proposals which are designed to drive their barge line competitors out of business.

The public interest is best served through cooperation of the various modes and retention of their individual identities under independent ownership and operation. Abundant proof exists that this is the only way that the various modes can add to the nation's strength, achieve economy for the consumers, and earn profits and goodwill for themselves.

16 National Defense

Inland waterways transportation is a recognized instrument of national defense as are the other modes.

The importance of the inland water carrier industry to the military defense of the country was dramatically demonstrated in World War II.

Since the war all phases of the inland waterways industry have improved equipment, facilities and operating techniques, adding measurably to defense capabilities.

The entire domestic transportation system, including the inland waterways, was placed under the control of the Of fice of Defense Transportation at the outbreak of World War II. The barge and towing vessel industry operated under the Inland Waterways Division of the Waterway Transport Department of the Office of Defense Transportation. This was one of three separate divisions of water transportation set up by executive order. Coastwise and intercoastal transport was handled by one division and the Great Lakes by another.

At the time the inland waterways fleet was mobilized it included 1,000 towboats and 5,000 barges operating over the Gulf Intracoastal Waterway from St. Marks, Florida, to Corpus Christi, Texas, the Mississippi-Illinois-Ohio River System, the Atlantic Intracoastal Waterway from Jacksonville, Florida, to Norfolk, Virginia, the New York State Barge Canal, smaller river tributaries of these main-stem waterway systems, and some Pacific Coast rivers.

Among the wartime achievements of inland waterways transportation was the movement of large quantities of strategic commodities, goods and supplies which were required for total war production. Many industries vital to the war effort could not have operated effectively without the availability of inland water transportation.

During the war period when enemy submarines blockaded coastal ports and were harassing the offshore shipping lanes with disastrous results, towboats, tugs and barges were called into service on the protected inland channels to deliver some 1,279,000 barrels of petroleum products daily. The heavy movement of petroleum by barge began early in World War II and has continued without interruption.

Military production planners relied heavily upon barges for many complete movements, but perhaps the outstanding role of the barges was that which they performed in combination with other modes of transportation. The water movements made by the barge lines in conjunction with pipelines, tank cars and tank trucks brought about the most efficient coordination of transportation facilities the country has ever seen.

Barges were credited with transporting a total of 1,731,030,485 barrels of petroleum and petroleum products during the war years, the equivalent of more than seven million tank car loads, representing 72,732 trains of 100 cars each.

In a review of the status of the inland water carrier industry at the conclusion of World War II, the Office of Defense Transportation said: "If our waterways rendered no service beyond that of transporting petroleum and its products during the war, they would have amply justified their improved existence."

Another remarkable wartime achievement of the inland waterways industry was in the shipbuilding and repair field. Under the impetus of World War II needs, inland shipbuilding and repair facilities were expanded from 85 to 140. Shipyards were built on practically all inland waterways where the construction of many different types of oceangoing vessels contributed much to the successful termination of the war.

This could be done only because it was possible to move these vessels from construction yards at inland points to the ocean via the inland waterways. Inland shipyards turned out more than 4,000 vessels including submarines, torpedo boat tenders, coastal transports, auxiliary repair ships, aircraft rescue vessels, destroyer escorts, barges, oceangoing cargo ships, floating cranes, Coast Guard cutters, patrol craft, subchasers, tugboats, tank ships and all types of military landing craft.

Tankers designed to deliver aviation gasoline to Navy fighting planes in all parts of the world were built in the wheat fields of Minnesota. Some of the Navy's largest submarines were built on Lake Michigan, at Manitowoc, Wisconsin, and taken under their own power to Chicago. There they were loaded into huge floating dry docks, especially designed for that purpose, for the long trip down the Illinois and Mississippi Rivers to the Gulf of Mexico where they were commissioned with Navy crews and sent off to join the fighting forces in the Pacific and elsewhere in the world.

Some 43,744 tons of structural ship sections were built at inland shipyards along or adjacent to the Ohio River.

War vessels constructed at inland points were successfully, safely, and efficiently moved to deep water over the inland waterways system. Many of them because of their drafts had to be pontooned or otherwise floated and towed to sea.

The facilities and the skills are still maintained in many of these yards today to service the large fleet of vessels now in use for river transportation and are of inestimable value to our defense effort and would be of even greater value in the event of attack.

Inland waterways transportation in World War II also made possible the desirable dispersal of essential war industries to the interior of the country and the easing of the burden placed upon other forms of transportation by increased traffic related to wartime production.

Traffic on the inland system slacked off with the reduction in wartime demands for transportation, but the industry continued to invest in improved equipment and make advances in its operating techniques which were indicated under the stress of national emergency.

Defense planners foresee the possibility of a vastly different type war as a consequence of the development of nuclear weapons and intercontinental ballistic missiles. The cold war, however, has focused attention upon the requirement for maximum efficiency in the utilization of transportation resources. Advances in inland water transportation and its better interlock with rail and highway networks provide assurance that prolonged national defense requirements can be met effectively and economically.

Records of The American Waterways Operators, Inc., show thousands of plants being constructed or undergoing expansion along the water routes since World War II. While these waterside locations may not have been chosen solely for the purpose of using low-cost barge services, the nation's water transportation routes continue to attract industrial production facilities.

Location of production facilities and terminaling facilities on waterside sites assures the availability of low-cost barge service at an average cost of three mills per ton-mile. This service is especially attractive for bulk-loading commodities, both dry and liquid.

Many industrial production facilities located on improved navigation channels also benefit directly from the availability of stable, adequate water supply for manufacturing processes which require it.

In recent years inland waterways transportation has been dramatically involved in the Nation's space exploration program. In the early years of the Saturn space exploration program, barge service was used to transport the space vehicle boosters built at the Marshall Space Flight Center in Huntsville, Alabama. No other means of transportation had the capability to move them. On its 2,261-mile journey to Cape Canaveral in Florida, the Saturn travelled by a special modified barge down the Tennessee River and the Ohio River to Cairo,

Illinois, where the Mississippi provided the route to New Orleans. From New Orleans to the Cape, the boosters were towed via the Gulf of Mexico.

At the same time, inland waterways transportation was called upon to move equipment and supplies of many types to top-priority space and defense projects scattered throughout the area served by inland channels. One of these was the National Aeronautics and Space Administration's large Michoud Assembly facility, 15 miles from downtown New Orleans on the Gulf Intracoastal Waterway. The Michoud site was selected because of its accessibility to water transportation. Forty miles by canal to the northeast of Michoud, in southern Mississippi, pine and cypress trees were bulldozed for construction of a $300-million site for ground testing of rocket stages and engines. The necessity of transporting the large space vehicle boosters built at Michoud via the inland waterways required the construction of a special barge dock at Michoud. Barges delivered rocket stages and engines directly to test stands, some of which were the tallest structures in Mississippi. Canals surrounded the test site, and waterways were improved in the area.

The Saturn space vehicle booster production operations were eventually moved to Michoud and continued there throughout the life of the Saturn program. The Saturn program was succeeded by NASA's space shuttle program which is now in the pilot stages and is expected to last perhaps as long as the turn of the century. Michoud is to be the assembly site for the large propellant tanks used in the space shuttle program and a variety of specially-built barges are used to transport these to the Florida launch site. Other equipment used in the program moved by water from California through the Panama Canal to Florida.

17 Water Recreation

One of the happiest and most widely appreciated public benefits of navigable rivers, canals, and lakes in the United States is their use for recreation. Whatever his pleasure, these navigable waterways offer much to the outdoorsman and his family.

Millions of pleasure craft users (estimated at about 46 million persons) crowd the waterways in the spring, summer, and fall months, using every conceivable type of craft from rafts and canoes to racy speed boats and sleek, high-powered yachts. More than nine million such craft are estimated in use.

Congress, to facilitate pleasure boating, has authorized and the Corps of Engineers has constructed a large number of small boat harbors which have been turned over to local interests to maintain and operate. States, counties, municipalities, private companies, and individuals have built launching, docking, and service facilities throughout the waterways system.

Canalization of navigable streams by the construction of dams and locks creates slack-water pools that are ideal for recreational boating. Construction of reservoirs in headwaters areas and along tributary streams creates idyllic lakes that draw water-sport enthusiasts.

Fish and wildlife conservation usually goes hand in hand with improvements for navigation. The slack-water reaches of navigation pools as well as the raceways immediately below the dams draw their coterie of anglers. For the more rugged, fishing and hunting is good along the navigable waterways and on headwaters lakes the year around. On the extreme northern waterways, ice fishing has become extremely popular. However, not all fishing is for fun. Commercial fishing plays an important part in the economy of many communities adjoining navigable waterways.

In the fall an added recreational opportunity becomes available to the outdoorsmen when the navigable rivers and canals provide wild fowl hunting for large armies of sportsmen in many areas of the country where the waterways become flyways during the migratory seasons. Thousands of acres of wild fowl habitat have been made available by the Corps of Engineers to the Bureau of Sport Fisheries and Wildlife of the United States Fish and Wildlife Service. These areas are managed as wild fowl refuges and are often open to the public for hunting and fishing.

While the recreational opportunities afforded by the navigable waterways are many and varied, they are not without hazards, especially for the small boat navigator. The waterways carry a large volume of commercial traffic, most of it moving in barges pushed ahead of powerful towboats. Such tows frequently exceed 1,000 feet in length and may be as much as 200 feet wide. Once under way they cannot be maneuvered sharply or stopped quickly, and small boat operators should be extremely cautious of them.

To stop the forward movement of a tow of barges, as in stopping any moving object, requires a certain amount of time and distance, in some cases as much as a half mile when a very large and heavy tow is involved. No small boat operator can be sure that his engine will not stall at any given time and should therefore allow himself plenty of leeway when crossing in front of a tow in order to avoid endangering himself, his passengers, and his craft. The same applies in the case of water skiers who could tumble or be thrown from their skis at any moment. While it may be exciting, it is folly for the operators of pleasure craft and for skiers to cross too closely in front of a tow of barges or to pass too closely down the sides of tows. Some skiers have even tried to go between the barges in a tow with fatal results.

The people who navigate the waterways for a living want very much to share the waters safely with their friends who use them for recreation and pleasure. And towing vessel crews will extend themselves to insure the safety of those in smaller vessels or on skis. But the pleasure craft operator and the skier must always bear in mind that a heavy tow maneuvers slowly and stops slowly; and further that the very presence in the water of vessels as big as a towboat and a barge creates danger. The suction or undertow around a towboat or barge, whether it is in motion or standing still, is a strong and dangerous force.

18 The Army Corps of Engineers

The Corps of Engineers, United States Army, has the responsibility under Congressional authorization for planning, improving, and maintaining the nation's navigable waterways, including the harbors.

The Corps has been associated with this work since 1824 when the Congress authorized the President to have surveys, plans and estimates made of roads and canals which he deemed of national importance from the commercial or military point of view or for the transportation of mail. To carry out this project, he was authorized to use the services of officers of the Corps of

Engineers. This authorization together with the appropriation the same year by Congress of $75,000 "for removing sand bars from the Ohio, and planters, sawyers and snags from the Mississippi" marked the beginning of the Federal Government assuming responsibility for improving the nation's navigation channels. In the same year, the first Federal appropriation was made for harbor improvements at the Harbor of Presque Isle on Lake Erie and Plymouth Beach on the New England Coast. Prior to that time there was no coordinated direction of work with respect to improvement of water resources for navigation. What little had been accomplished was done by Federal, state and local agencies and private interests without any attempt at standardization or coordination.

For almost a century and a half, the Army Corps of Engineers has had the responsibility for constructing, maintaining and operating U. S. inland waterways, including harbors, for commercial navigation. The responsibility includes engineering feasibility studies, cost studies, economic analysis, and development of overall justification data as a basis for Congressional action to authorize and finance river and harbor improvements.

In addition, the Corps has full engineering and construction management responsibility for the following work:

1. Providing and maintaining channels at their authorized depth and width;
2. Improving and maintaining harbors, including providing protective works such as jetties and breakwaters;
3. Providing means other than lighting and marking of channels for facilitating navigation;
4. Canalization where locks and dams are required;
5. Removal of obstructions to maintain the navigability of the waterways.

Congressional authorization for this work is voted in River and Harbor Acts, sometimes referred to as Omnibus Authorization Acts. They also contain authorizations for flood control, beach erosion control work, multiple-purpose projects involving water use, and related projects.

Since the initial acts of 1824 authorizing improvements and appropriating funds, virtually every succeeding Congress has passed one or more acts providing for maintenance and improvement of rivers and harbors. These general acts usually contain two principal items: one authorizes work of improvement of specific rivers and harbors in accordance with engineering and economic feasibility reports previously submitted by the Corps of Engineers; and the other authorizes surveys for such work at designated localities.

Prior to 1922, in addition to approving specific projects, River and Harbor Acts also appropriated the money for construction. With the passage of the Act of 1922, River and Harbor Acts have contained only provisions giving Congressional authority to proceed with certain projects; and funds to carry out the work have been provided in separate public work appropriation bills.

There is a great body of law dealing with the development and use of inland waters. Some of the significant legislation affecting the responsibility of the Corps of Engineers is worthy of attention since it provides the continuing policy guidance for both the legislative and executive branches of the government.

An Act of June 28, 1879, established the Mississippi River Commission whose duties are to conduct surveys of the Mississippi River, to consider and mature plans to locate permanently and deepen the channels for the improvement and safety of navigation, to promote and facilitate commerce, trade and postal service and to prevent destructive floods. The Commission consists of three officers of the Corps of Engineers, one from the U. S. Coast and Geodetic Survey, and three members from civil life, two of whom are civil engineers. All members are appointed by the President with the advice and consent of the Senate. An officer of the Corps of Engineers is designated as the President of the Commission and serves as its executive officer. An officer of the Corps is assigned to serve as secretary of the Commission in the office of its president. Headquarters of the Commission are in Vicksburg, Mississippi.

In order to determine the amount of commerce using navigable waters, the Corps of Engineers by an act of February 21, 1891, was authorized to collect statistics at points of arrival and departure of vessels, regarding passengers, freight and tonnage carried. Further, Section 500 of the Transportation Act of February 28, 1920, provided for the compilation, publication and distribution of statistics, data and information concerning transportation on inland waterways as might be deemed of value to the commercial interests of the country.

The principal provision governing the collection of these data was subsequently embodied in the River and Harbar Act of 1922. Section 11 of that Act provides "That owners, agents, master and clerks of vessels and other craft plying upon the navigable waters of the United States, and all individuals and corporations engaged in transporting their own goods upon the navigable waters of the United States, shall furnish such statements relative to vessels, passengers, freight and tonnage as may be required by the Secretary of War: Provided, That this provision shall not apply to those rafting logs, except upon a direct request upon the owner to furnish specific information."

This information is compiled to meet the administrative requirements of the Department of the Army in connection with the duties assigned by Congress, and provides vital data for other governmental departments, commercial and shipping concerns, and others interested in transportation.

Congress by an Act of March 3, 1899, provided for the protection of navigation by prohibiting the discharge or dumping of refuse matter of any kind or description, other than that flowing from streets and sewers, into any navigable water or tributary thereto.

The improvement of any navigable river by persons, corporations or municipalities, at their expense and risk, was authorized by the Act of June 13, 1902, which set the stage for a great number of private construction projects such as piers, jetties, and breakwaters. This act stipulates that such work of improvement must conform with the Federal plan of Government improvement and that the plans and specifications therefor must be approved by the Office of the Secretary of War (which later became the Office of the Secretary of the Army), and the Chief of Engineers.

The Board of Engineers for Rivers and Harbors was established by Section 3 of the River and Harbor Act of June 13, 1902. This is a board of seven Engineer officers (it originally had five members) whose duties are to review all reports on authorized preliminary examinations and surveys of river and harbor projects and to report its conclusions and recommendations to the Chief of Engineers who forwards the report with his conclusions and recommendations to the Secretary of the Army for transmittal to Congress. Later this procedure was amended to apply also to flood control reports. The Board is also authorized, when requested by the appropriate committees of Congress,

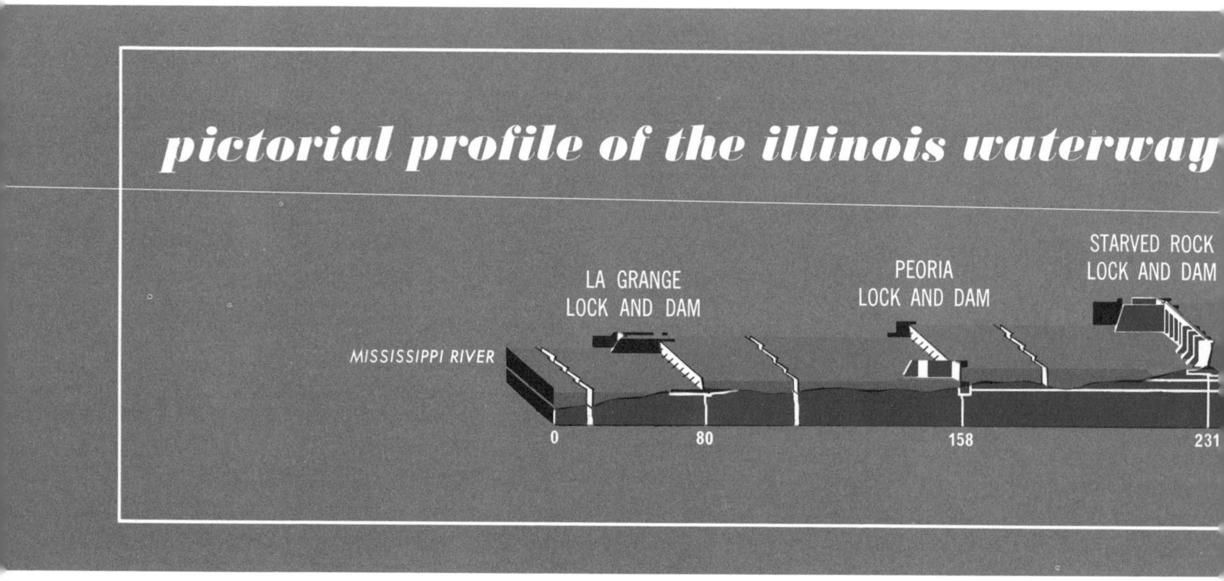

to review and report through the Chief of Engineers upon any authorized project or desired improvement with a view to recommending the initiation of a project or modification of an existing project. The Chief of Engineers may refer to the Board for consideration and recommendation all special reports ordered by Congress and may prescribe such other duties as he desires. Members of the Board consist of a senior member, generally the Deputy Chief of Engineers, five officers who are usually Division Engineers assigned to Board membership in addition to their other duties, and a resident member permanently stationed for his tour of duty with the Board in Washington, D. C.

Under an Act of March 4, 1913, procedures were established to determine which of proposed river and harbor projects are worthy of improvement at Federal expense. Here are a few of the detailed steps that must be taken to get a project into actual construction.

1. Local interests, after deciding that a waterways project will be beneficial in stimulating commerce, draft a request for improvement and send it to their representatives in the Congress.

2. If a Congressman finds the project has sufficient merit, he individually or in concert with his colleagues will transmit the proposal to the Public Works Committee of the House of Representatives with a request that the committee authorize the Corps of Engineers to investigate and report its findings. If the project has been previously reported on, the Committee may request by its own resolution that the Board of Engineers for Rivers and Harbors review or update previous reports. Normally, this additional study will be assigned to the District Engineer for the area in which the project is located. If the proposal is a new project, it must be included in a River and Harbor Act authorizing and directing the Secretary of the Army to

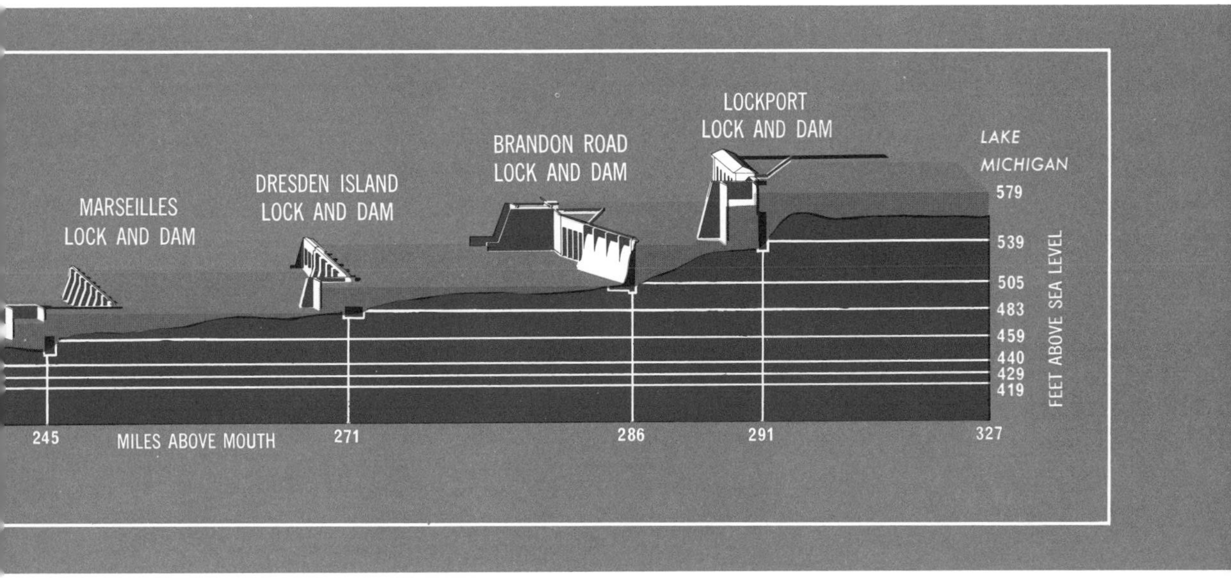

have a preliminary examination and survey made of the desired project.

3. After authorization of a project by the Congress, the District Engineer's first concern is the preliminary economic justification of the project. This is largely determined through public hearings and the findings are sent to the Division Engineer for examination and forwarding to the Board of Engineers for Rivers and Harbors.

4. If the District Engineer's preliminary report is favorable and the Board concurs, the District Engineer is authorized to proceed with a survey. If the District Engineer's preliminary survey is unfavorable or if the Board of Engineers for Rivers and Harbors fails to concur in a favorable report, the Public Works Committee is advised and the project is dead. It can be brought up again, however, under the same locally initiated procedure.

5. The District Engineer makes a detailed survey on the basis of approval of the preliminary report by the Board. Plans, specifications and cost estimates are prepared and a report made on the expected benefits and savings which justify the project.

6. The Board makes a thorough review of every aspect of the project, and may call for additional studies and hearings. If the Board finds the survey report in order and if the public benefits exceed the cost of construction, maintenance and amortization, the Board approves the report and sends it to the Chief of Engineers.

7. The Chief of Engineers then prepares an overall report which is submitted to the governors of the affected states and interested Federal agencies, including the Bureau of the Budget, for their views.

8. Next the report goes to the Secretary of the Army who presents it to the Public Works Committee of the House

of Representatives which has it printed as a public document; and the project is included in the next River and Harbor Authorization bill on which public hearings are held.

9. When this bill is enacted by the House of Representatives and by the Senate and signed by the President, the project becomes an authorized project and is ready for construction.

10. The next step is for the Chief of Engineers to make a request for funds through the Secretary of the Army. The request is reviewed by the Bureau of the Budget.

11. If the Bureau finds the request conforms to the operating policy plans of the President, it is included in the President's Budget. Budget requests for inland waterways and harbor improvements are included in a Public Works Appropriation bill which originates in the House of Representatives and is subject to detailed review and consideration by a subcommittee of the House Appropriations Committee. During this review and consideration, the Corps of Engineers is called upon to explain and justify every dollar requested. The Bureau of the Budget and interested individuals and organizations are given an opportunity to testify for or against the needs for the various projects included in the bill. A favorable report by the Civil Functions Subcommittee is subject to further review by the full Appropriations Committee before presentation to the House of Representatives for consideration.

12. Passage by the House opens the way for consideration and review by the Senate Appropriations Committee and its subcommittee and then by the Senate itself. Upon passage by the Senate and resolution of any differences between the House and Senate versions, the Public Works Appropriation bill goes to the President for his signature.

13. When funds are appropriated, they are given to the cognizant District Engineer for expenditure in preparing plans and specifications, which must proceed through the Engineer's chain of command and control for final approval, and for construction which is accomplished through a competitive bidding system by private contractors. The present practice of the Congress is to appropriate funds piecemeal, giving the Corps of Engineers only enough funds to proceed on a project for 12 months, thereby subjecting each project to continuous review until its completion.

To keep a project alive through repeated stages of survey, report, recommendation, review, authorization and through step by step appropriation of funds, vigorous, constant and continuing public support is necessary.

An Act of March 4, 1915 authorized the Chief of Engineers to establish anchorage grounds for vessels in all harbors, rivers and bays, and other navigable waters of the United States, wherever it is determined that the maritime or commercial interests of the United States require such anchorage grounds for safe navigation.

Strictly speaking the Corps of Engineers comprises the engineer officers and men of the United States Army who carry out a primary military mission, but the Corps serves also as the Federal agent for a wide variety of civil works, including waterways and harbor improvements. The Corps has a large staff of civilian employees. For operating purposes the Corps of Engineers is headed by the Chief of Engineers whose headquarters is in Washington, D. C. The field work is carried out by 12 division offices and over 40 district offices.

The Corps of Engineers works mainly through private contractors for construction, development, operation and maintenance of the improved rivers, canals, and harbors. However, the Corps operates a fleet of almost 3,000 vessels consisting of dredges, barges, pontoons and other floating equipment to carry out certain continuing maintenance and operation work.

Congress also has given the Corps the responsibility for performing many other functions related to navigation. The Corps must approve and issue permits for any structures to be built along the navigable streams which would in any way affect navigability, such as docks and moorings, and structures over and under navigable streams, except bridges and causeways. The Corps can, where and when deemed necessary, restrict the size of tows and impose restrictions on speed of vessels.

The Corps' Division and District Engineer offices issue navigation bulletins as required by channel conditions. These reports contain the latest information regarding channel depth, condition, sailing directions, special notices, and any other information to aid navigation.

Under its broad responsibility to maintain the navigability of the waters of the United States as well as under specific statutes, the Corps of Engineers is charged with responsibility to prevent pollution. Formerly, the Corps' water pollution authority was more extensive, but much of the authority with respect to vessel pollution has been made the responsibility of the Coast Guard under the Federal Water Pollution Control Act.

The jurisdiction of the Department of the Army, exercised through the Corps of Engineers, is usually limited and directed in actual enforcement to such control as may be necessary to prevent any act whereby the public right of navigation shall or may be impeded or obstructed. However, far broader interpretations of the laws have been rendered by Federal court decisions in the interest of preserving navigable waters for maximum utilization by the general public for business, recreation or other purposes.

The Federal anti-pollution laws extend to all navigable waters, whether tidal or non-tidal, below the high water mark, and to the deposit of material on river banks or in branch streams and on the decks of towboats and/or barges where it is liable to be washed into navigable waters. The coastal waters of the United States are included to such distance seaward as may be necessary to give full effect to the laws for the protection and preservation of navigable waters.

The Refuse Act of 1899 makes it unlawful to discharge any refuse into navigable waters of the United States or into any waters where it may float or be washed into navigable waters, except in authoritatively designated areas under prescribed regulations. The Secretary of the Army, acting through the Corps of Engineers, also has responsibility for enforcement of this Act which provides for fines not to exceed $2,500 nor less than $500 and/or for imprisonment of violators.

19 Interstate Commerce Commission

Certain inland water carrier operations are subject to regulation by the Interstate Commerce Commission.

Congress created the Interstate Commerce Commission as an independent agency of the Federal Government to regulate the transportation of passengers and goods from one state to another on February 4, 1887, in An Act to Regulate Commerce.

The original act, now known as the Interstate Commerce Act, was confined to the regulation of interstate commerce by railroad, or partly by railroad and partly by water. It was a very brief statute of less than 10 pages. After some 200 amendments or modifications the same law and related acts today fill over 600 pages.

The ICC staff consists of almost 1,700 employees in its Washington, D. C., headquarters and various fields. The 11 ICC commissioners are appointed by the President with the advice and consent of the Senate for seven-year terms or to fill unexpired terms.

Under Reorganization Plan No. 1 of 1969, the President was given the authority as of January 1, 1970, to name a permanent ICC chairman. Previously the Commission had selected its own chairman, who served in that capacity for a year, from among the Commissioners. The Commissioners still elect a vice chairman on an annual basis.

Not all domestic transportation is regulated by the ICC. Transportation performed wholly within a single state and not part of an interstate or foreign movement is regulated by the state government. The Civil Aeronautics Board and the Federal Aviation Agency have jurisdiction over air transportation. The Federal Power Commission regulates gas pipelines. Ships in foreign service are regulated by the Federal Maritime Commission.

About 17,580 for-hire companies providing domestic surface transportation are subject to ICC regulation. They include the railroads, trucking companies, bus lines, barge and other inland and coastal shipping companies, oil pipelines, freight forwarders, and express companies. Their annual operating revenues total more than $33.9 billion.

In broad terms and within prescribed legal limits, ICC regulation encompasses both economics and service. The agency settles controversy over rates and services among competing forms of transportation, shippers and receivers of freight, travelers and others; regulates mergers or sales of carriers, and issuance of their securities; prescribes accounting rules; awards reparations; administers acts to prevent undue discrimination, preference or prejudice, destructive competition, and rebating.

Upon a showing of public convenience and necessity, ICC issues operating franchises to trucking companies, bus lines, freight forwarders, water carriers, and transportation brokers, and approves applications to construct or abandon lines of railroads. It also designates the time-zone boundaries, and compiles statistics of carriers' revenues and expenses.

Carriers initiate their own rate proposals, filing more than 200,000 of them each year to become effective upon 30 days' notice to the public as required by law. The Commission intervenes in only about two percent of these proposals, nearly always after a protest is received from the public or from competing carriers and it suspends the proposed rates in less than half of these cases. Usually rates go into effect exactly as proposed by the carriers.

The Transportation Act of 1940 (Part III of the Interstate Commerce Act) brought under regulation by the Interstate Commerce Commission certain kinds of inland water carrier transportation which the Congress at that time viewed as being competitive with rail transportation, mainly transportation of mark and count commodities. The 1940 legislation also established the present National Transportation Policy. This policy, a preamble to the Interstate Commerce Act, states:

"It is hereby declared to be the national transportation policy of the Congress to provide for fair and impartial regulation of all modes of transportation subject to the provisions of this

Act, so administered as to recognize and preserve the inherent advantages of each; to promote safe, adequate, economical, and efficient service and foster sound economic conditions in transportation and among the several carriers; to encourage the establishment and maintenance of reasonable charges for transportation services, without unjust discriminations, undue preferences or advantages, or unfair or destructive competitive practices; to cooperate with the several States and the duly authorized officials thereof; and to encourage fair wages and equitable working conditions; all to the end of developing, coordinating, and preserving a national transportation system by water, highway, and rail, as well as other means, adequate to meet the needs of the commerce of the United States, of the Postal Service, and of the national defense. All of the provisions of this Act shall be administered and enforced with a view to carrying out the above declaration of policy."

The effect of Part III of the Interstate Commerce Act is to make those inland water carriers subject to ICC regulation who hold themselves out for hire as common carriers providing regular service over specified routes and at specified ports of call. They must have a certificate issued by the Interstate Commerce Commission. They are subject to the economic regulatory authority of the Commission, and are required, among other things, to file and publish their tariffs, and submit financial reports.

The Interstate Commerce Commission is also given authority over issuance and supervision of towing rights in certain instances as well as authority over certain types of contract water carrier operations.

In passing Part III of the Interstate Commerce Act, the Congress spelled out certain exemptions from economic regulation for water carriers. Section 303 (b) exempts the transportation by a water carrier of commodities in bulk when the cargo space of the vessel in which such commodities are transported is used for the carrying of not more than three such commodities. This section applies in the case of commodities in bulk which are loaded and carried without wrappers or containers and received and delivered by the carrier without transportation mark or count. For the purposes of this section of Part III, two or more vessels (towboats, tugs and barges) when operated as a unit, as in a tow, are considered to be a single vessel.

Section 303 (d) of Part III of the Interstate Commerce Act exempts from economic regulation the transportation by water of liquid cargoes carried in bulk in tank vessels designed for use exclusively in such service and certificated for such service.

Only about 10 percent of the commodities transported in vessels on inland channels are regulated by ICC. The other 90 percent of the tonnage is either exempt for-hire service or private transportation. Many regulated carriers, in addition to providing service under their ICC certificates, also engage in exempt operations.

The question of transportation regulation versus exemption has been a source of controversy for many years. Regulated water carriers generally favor repeal of the dry bulk commodity exemption provisions of the Interstate Commerce Act. The exempt carriers—both those engaged in transporting nonregulated dry bulk commodities and those transporting liquids—generally oppose any extension of regulation. They believe that a change in regulation to bring either dry bulk or liquid bulk commodities under ICC regulation will increase the price of service, diminish flexibility of operations, and make it unreasonably difficult for them to compete for business.

20 United States Coast Guard

The United States Coast Guard's responsibilities encompass numerous activities affecting operations on the inland waterways.

This agency's mission is to insure the safety of persons and property in the use of the waters. It is a complex undertaking involving law enforcement, including enforcement of the Federal Water Pollution Control Act and amendments thereto, search and rescue, as well as the establishment of navigation regulations and the establishment and maintenance of physical aids to navigation.

Under provisions of the Department of Transportation Act, which was signed into Public Law 89-670, the Coast Guard, after nearly 177 years in the Treasury Department, on April 1, 1967 was transferred to the new Department of Transportation. The transfer did not affect the overall mission or the general operations of the Coast Guard in the exercise of its responsibilities as they affect the barge and towing industry.

The Coast Guard was transferred as an entity with the Commandant reporting directly to the Secretary of Transportation. The transfer meant the addition of new responsibilities for the agency. Certain duties of the Army Corps of Engineers dealing with the operation of drawbridges, anchorages and oil pollution laws were made Coast Guard responsibilities. The Great Lakes Pilotage Administration was made part of the Coast Guard and assigned to the Commander, Ninth Coast Guard District at Cleveland, Ohio. A number of duties of the Customs Bureau were also assigned to the Coast Guard.

The barge and towing industry worked closely with the Coast Guard in the development of a bill to license pilothouse personnel aboard certain vessels. The bill was passed by the House on April 29, 1971 and by the Senate on June 2, 1972 with an amendment to exclude from coverage vessels of less than 200 gross tons engaging in service to the offshore oil and mineral exploitation industry. The Act, (Public Law 92-339), provides that "an uninspected towing vessel [26 feet or more in length] in order to assure safe navigation shall, while underway, be under the actual direction and control of a person licensed by the Secretary [of Transportation] to operate in the particular geographic area and by the type of vessel under regulations prescribed by him." It stipulates that "a person so licensed may not work a vessel while underway or perform other duties in excess of a total of 12 hours in any consecutive 24-hour period except in case of emergency." The regulations to implement the pilothouse licensing act became effective in September 1973.

Under the Federal Water Pollution Control Act and amendments thereto, the Coast Guard was designated to develop and promulgate new regulations designed to minimize oil pollution from vessels and loading facilities. Most of the rules were designed to become effective on July 1, 1974.

Among the fundamentals to safe use of the waters are the Rules of the Road which govern the operation of vessels. Operations on the inland waterways (exclusive of the Great Lakes) are governed by two sets of such rules. Shallow-draft vessel operators from time to time become subject to two other sets. The Western Rivers Rules of the Road and the Inland Rules of the Road are both established by statute and by Coast

The Coast Guard provides the traffic guides on U.S. waters.

Guard regulations and control operations on inland channels exclusive of the Great Lakes. The term "Western Rivers" applies to the Mississippi River system and its tributaries down to the Huey P. Long Bridge at New Orleans. Vessel operations on all other inland channels except the Great Lakes are controlled by the Inland Rules. The Great Lakes Rules of the Road are also a combination of laws and regulations and control operations on the Great Lakes. The International Rules governing operations on the high seas are established by international treaty and are also enacted into United States statutes.

Rules of the Road not only govern the physcal handling of vessels but establish procedures for the lighting of vessels for recognition purposes during the periods when the vessels are in motion, tied up, or anchored. They regulate moorings and anchorings to insure the safety of persons and property both with respect to the moored or anchored vessel and for other vessels that may be navigating in the vicinity.

Obviously the four sets of rules create problems. For example, a towing vessel starting a voyage from the lake front in Chicago and going to Tampa, Florida will start its voyage under Great Lakes Rules, go under Western Rivers Rules at a point in the Chicago area, pass from the jurisdiction of Western Rivers Rules to the jurisdiction of the Inland Rules at the Huey P. Long Bridge over the Mississippi River in the New Orleans area, and then become subject to International Rules as it crosses the Gulf of Mexico. Similar situations apply in many other instances.

A concerted effort is being made to unify the Rules of the Road. It is generally acknowledged that a single set of rules, with certain local rules incorporated where necessitated by special circumstances, would enhance safety of navigation.

The Coast Guard maintains more than 44,000 aids to navigation, approximately 24,000 of which are buoy markers on the inland waterways of the United States.

Other aids to navigation which the Coast Guard maintains include conventional lighthouses, offshore platform light stations, lightships, radiobeacons, fog signals, daybeacons, and long-range electronic aids.

Their cost and complexity vary from a simple river buoy costing less than a hundred dollars to a multi-million dollar LORAN station.

Under the Tanker Act the Coast Guard in 1936 promulgated rules and regulations for tank vessels which cover in detail the construction, maintenance, inspection, manning, and operation of such vessels for safety purposes. The Tanker Act was amended by the Ports and Waterways Safety Act of 1972 to extend this authority for environmental purposes and to impose both civil and criminal sanctions for violations of the law.

Regulations have also been established pursuant to the Dangerous Cargoes Act of 1940 governing the carriage of inflammable and combustible liquids, liquefied inflammable gases, and other dangerous commodities in drums, barrels, cases, and other packages.

In the exercise of its authority to maintain safe use of the waters for the transportation of dangerous cargoes, the Coast Guard regulations cover every detail of the construction and operation of tank vessels, including in certain instances precautionary regulations with respect to the speed at which certain tank barges may be towed and their relationship to other barges in the makeup of a tow. These regulations are under constant revision.

All tank barges require certification by the Coast Guard and this certification prescribes and limits the use of the vessel. Such vessels are inspected during construction to insure compliance with applicable regulations and to insure that their construction is in accordance with plans approved by the Coast Guard. Periodically, after being placed in service, tank barges are inspected as a prerequisite to renewal of the certificate of inspection.

Practically all vessels used in towing service are motor vessels powered by diesel engines and diesel-powered vessels are not subject to inspection by the Coast Guard except in the cases of seagoing vessels of 300 gross tons or over. Existing law requires inspection and certification of all steam-powered towing vessels. The Coast Guard as a part of the certification of steam towing vessels prescribes manning scales, i.e., the number of personnel required to operate the vessel, and establishes the qualifications and licenses the operating personnel.

Diesel-powered towing vessels must meet other types of safety requirements. Load lines are required for vessels of 150 gross tons or over if they are in the coastwise or Great Lakes trade or if they are going on foreign sea voyages. All towing vessels must meet the requirements of law and Coast Guard regulations for uninspected vessels with respect to lifesaving and fire fighting equipment precautionary measures, ground tackle, hawsers, and bilge systems, including requirements to carry life preservers and fire extinguishers approved by the Coast Guard in such numbers as the Coast Guard specifies.

All towing vessels, of course, are subject to the Rules of the Road applicable to the waters on which they are operating. In carrying out its law enforcement responsibilities the Coast Guard has authority to board any vessel on the navigable waters of the United States.

Coast Guard regulations require that tows carrying inflammable or combustible liquids in bulk have on board a licensed officer or certificated tankerman with a certificate endorsed to show he is qualified to handle the grade of cargo carried. The Coast Guard maintains control over licenses and certificates which it issues to seamen by investigating acts of misconduct, negligence, and incompetence and may bring charges before an examiner for the purpose of seeking to revoke or suspend such licenses or certificates.

The United States Coast Guard administers three special statutes having to do with the transportation of dangerous cargoes on the navigable waters, including loading and unloading operations. Certain provisions of the Tanker Act apply to vessels carrying combustible or inflammable liquid cargo in bulk and the Coast Guard has established regulations dealing with the design, construction, and operations of tank barges and tank ships. Provisions of the Dangerous Cargo Act apply to all vessels carrying such cargoes and Coast Guard regulations set forth requirements and conditions governing the carriage of all dangerous cargoes aboard all vessels except those subject to the Tanker Act when such vessels are operating in the territorial waters of the United States. The Commandant of the Coast Guard also has responsibilities under terms of the Espionage Act and has issued regulations for the handling of dangerous cargoes on waterfront facilities and on board vessels and for the control of movements of vessels in order to insure the safety of ports, vessels, and waterfront facilities.

Under the Espionage Act and Dangerous Cargoes Act the Coast Guard has been delegated broad authority to maintain a port security program to reduce injury to U. S. vessels, waterfront facilities and waters and can and does require that vessel personnel and others working in certain port areas obtain and carry prescribed identification papers.

Since 1936 the Coast Guard has been authorized to carry on ice-breaking operations to keep open certain channels and harbors, including such inland waterways as Chesapeake Bay, the Potomac River, the Illinois Waterway, and other areas.

The Coast Guard is required by law to investigate all marine casualties where a vessel of any kind is involved. Regulations require the owner, agent, master, or person in charge of a vessel involved in a marine casualty to report whenever a casualty results in actual physical damage to vessels or property in excess of $1,500, material damage affecting the seaworthiness or efficiency of a vessel, groundings, all losses of life, and injuries incapacitating in excess of 72 hours.

The Coast Guard administers a broad program for recreational boating safety, including administration of the Federal Boat Safety Act which was passed by the Congress in 1971. The Act provides, among other things, fines for negligent or reckless operators of motorboats and specifies minimum safety and signal equipment which must be carried.

About half the activities of the Coast Guard are devoted to Search and Rescue work. In an average year the Coast Guard will save some 3,000 lives, answer 60,000 calls for assistance, and save or help protect $2 billion of property.

The Coast Guard carries out an extensive cooperative program for the promotion of the safe use of the waters of the United States. The barge and towing industry cooperates wholeheartedly in this work and in addition carries out programs of its own. The Coast Guard Auxiliary plays an important role in the promotion of safety, including training in the operation of vessels and rescue and lifesaving work. Founded in 1941, the Auxiliary membership includes owners of boats, aircraft, radio stations, and others; state boating authorities; safety officials; United States Power Squadrons; the American Red Cross; and others.

The laws relating to the Coast Guard's authority and responsibility were codified by the Congress in 1949 with enactment of Title 14 of the United States Code.

The Coast Guard is one of the oldest service branches of the Federal Government with a history going back to August 4, 1790. As we know it today, however, the Coast Guard was created in 1915 with the consolidation of the Revenue Cutter Service (formerly Revenue Marine) and the Lifesaving Service, both of which had functioned separately within the Treasury Department for more than a century. Since 1915 the Coast Guard has been given additional duties and responsibilities, including the assignment of law enforcement powers on the high seas and navigable waters of the United States. The Lighthouse Service was transferred to the Coast Guard in 1939. The Bureau of Marine Inspection and Navigation was also transferred to the Coast Guard in 1942.

The Coast Guard displays and publishes storm warnings issued by the Weather Bureau. Cutters are assigned to maintain six ocean stations, two at fixed locations in the Pacific Ocean and four in the Atlantic, which regularly relay meteorological data to assist the Weather Bureau in its forecasting work. These cutters also provide important communications, navigation and search and rescue services to aircraft and vessels.

By executive order in 1946 the Commandant of the Coast Guard was given authority to establish panels of senior Coast Guard officers and advisors whose principal job is to evaluate all proposals for changes in regulations affecting the marine industry. During World War II the Western Rivers Panel was established within the Merchant Marine Council of the Coast Guard and charged by the Commandant "to receive problems referred to it from the Coast Guard affecting Western Rivers operations (the Mississippi River and its tributaries) and render advice, comments, criticisms or recommendations." In March 1971 the Merchant Marine Council was renamed the Marine Safety Council. Also in 1971 the Western Rivers Panel was reconstituted as the Towing Industry Advisory Committee to the Marine Safety Council to include all sections of the nation. The Committee, as did the Western Rivers Panel, may take the initiative in presenting its problems to the Coast Guard.

The Coast Guard operates under a Commandant, who is appointed to a four-year term by the President of the United States. The appointment is subject to confirmation by the Senate. His headquarters are located in Washington, D.C. The Coast Guard carries out its duties through 12 Coast Guard Districts, each operating under a district commander. In wartime or at the direction of the President, the Coast Guard is transferred from control of the Transportation Department to the Navy Department.

21 The Maritime Administration

In October 1971 the Maritime Administration established a new Office of Domestic Shipping to promote all segments of the domestic shipping industry and to end what officials of that agency termed "the apathy and neglect that have characterized the government's attitude for the domestic shipping industry."

Three separate divisions were created in the new office dealing with (1) the inland waterways trades, (2) the coastwise, non-contiguous and intercoastal trades, and (3) the Great Lakes trades.

This action implemented the long-standing mandate of the Merchant Marine Act of 1936, as amended, for the Maritime Administration to promote a merchant marine "sufficient to carry its domestic waterborne commerce . . . and to provide shipping service on all routes essential to maintaining the flow of such domestic . . . waterborne commerce at all times." This directive was given new impetus by the Merchant Marine Act of 1970, which specifies the extension of benefits to the entire merchant marine, including the barge and towing industry.

After preliminary informal meetings with individual domestic shipping groups, MARAD sponsored a National Planning Conference on Domestic Shipping from April 30 to May 4, 1972 in St. Louis, Missouri. The purpose of the conference was to identify industry needs and define goals for an effective program to meet them. A major objective of this "working conference" was to insure that the long-range program initiated by the Maritime Administration would be fully responsive to the needs of the industry. This was the first coordinated effort by responsible representatives of management, labor and Government to define the current and future problems faced by the nation's waterborne domestic shipping industry.

As a result of the conference, a recommended five-year program was developed which will eventually constitute a new national domestic shipping program.

Currently, the Office of Domestic Shipping plays a key role within the government as an "ombudsman" for the domestic shipping industry. Extending to the field of legislation, the best interests of the industry are brought to the attention of agencies whose actions may have an impact on the industry's operations. In addition, the Office of Domestic Shipping provides a forum in which problems of mutual concern in the industry can be discussed and in which new ideas for improved equipment and services can be explored and evaluated.

A substantive research and development program supports promotion of domestic shipping as well as the more traditional aspects of Maritime Administration programs. The necessity of achieving productivity gains in vessel construction and operations through technological advancement is the basis for this assistance to the maritime community.

In the area of financial assistance programs, the Maritime Administration, acting for the Secretary of Commerce, administers the Title XI Program which guarantees principal and interest payments on commercial obligations for eligible vessels. The program covers financing and refinancing for the construction, reconstruction or reconditioning of towboats and barges meeting certain criteria. A separate financial assistance program permits establishment of a capital construction fund with the Secretary of Commerce which makes certain tax deferral benefits available for construction of vessels in foreign trade, Great Lakes trade, the domestic non-contiguous trade and in the fisheries, but not to vessels in the coastal, intracoastal and inland waterways trade.

Joint efforts with industry and other government agencies have resulted in the creation of a computerized data bank for domestic commodity movements, traffic patterns and transport forecasts. These will aid the domestic shipping industry in pinpointing new markets and balancing out existing trades.

22

Waterway Economics

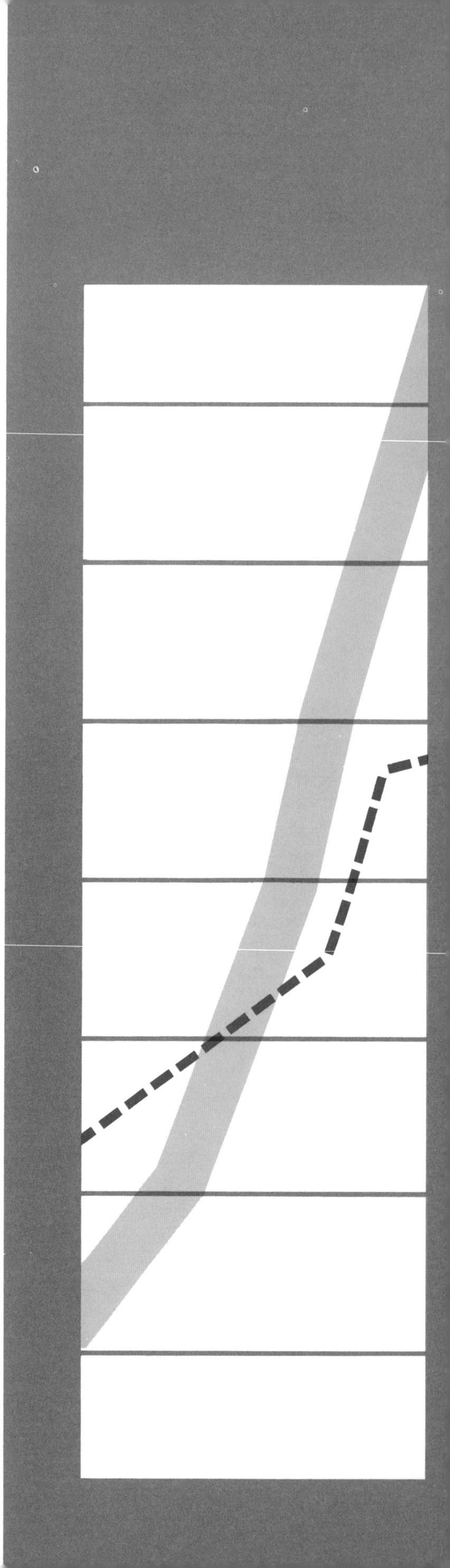

The Inland Waterways and Economic Growth

A good economist approaches his problems with just the right combination of skepticism and open-mindedness. Over a period of years, the spokesmen for water transportation have been pointing out the large volume of industrial development along the nation's inland waterways. The Ohio Valley Improvement Association reports a total investment of $36.9 billion in major plant construction and expansion projects, from 1950 through 1970, in counties bordering the Ohio River and its navigable tributaries. The records of The American Waterways Operators, Inc., show the construction or expansion of 8,742 plants, terminals, industrial parks, and port districts at water-oriented locations throughout the country from 1952 through 1972. Economists have been asking, "Does all this really mean that water transportation is a big stimulus to industrial growth? Or, does it mean something else?"

Suppose we were to ask the executives of a waterside plant, "Was water transportation really an important factor in your decision to locate or expand here?" For many, it was obviously important, and they will say so. The continuous big growth in waterborne tonnages of petroleum and petroleum products, chemicals, fertilizers, coal, scrap iron, steel, and other commodities has been matched by expansion of waterside plants shipping and unloading these commodities directly at the plant site.

In the Ohio Valley, for example, from 1950 through 1970, chemical companies built new waterside plants representing a total investment of $3.5 billion. Side by side with this investment, shipments of chemicals and products on the Ohio River jumped from 1.0 million tons per year to 10.6 million tons, a development integral with the plant site selections. The growth of waterborne utility coal has likewise been matched by a growth in the generating capacity of waterside stations, oftentimes built in conjunction with long-term waterborne coal contracts. The pattern repeats itself in a number of industries.

But, other waterside plant executives would say, "No, we actually don't ship or receive much by water". Does this mean that water transportation had nothing to do with the location of these plants? Often not. Water transportation commonly lies unseen behind the conscious reasons for the waterside location, particularly when the site was chosen with a view to ready availability by rail or truck of essential materials and fuels at low cost, such as steel, chemicals, or fuel oil. Some executives will cite low-cost electric energy as an important attraction.

The low-cost materials and fuels which draw new plants to a locality are often, themselves, the products of water-based industries. For example, a large appliance factory was built a short distance inland from the river in a waterside county. Water transportation was, at best, secondary in this site selection. But, among the important considerations was the low-cost availability of large tonnage materials—brought in from nearby origins by rail and truck—and these included steel and chemical products. The steel mills of the region received most of their coking coal by barge, and the steel product line locally available was more diverse by virtue of the broadened market made accessible by steel barging. A similar observation would have applied to chemical products and electric energy.

Aluminum plants are another illustration. From 1957 to 1971, 30 percent of all the new aluminum reduction capacity in the country was constructed on the banks of the Ohio River. River barging carries aluminum ores and concentrates to these plants. But this advantage has been only a contributing factor in the choice of location. The more critical influence was low-cost electricity. Some 60 percent of all the coal consumed by electric generating stations in the Ohio Valley is received by water.

Thus water-based industries, heavily dependent on water transportation, such as steel, chemicals, and electric power, tend to generate "satellite" industries in the vicinity. Sometimes these "satellites", as in the case of the appliance factory and the aluminum industry, challenge the water-shipping industries in scale. Water transportation may not have been the direct reason for the satellite location. But, even if not explicitly recognized, water carriage has been no less a factor by virtue of its indirectness.

But what about the firm which neither uses waterborne materials nor materials supplied by water-based industries? Such a plant is typically sandwiched between the river on one side and the railroad tracks on the other—with a good highway just across the railroad tracks. Not surprisingly, railroad rates to and from this plant are low. But they would not stay low very long if the river channel were blocked. Railroad rates are held at low levels because of competition on the waterway. For example, in a typical rail rate increase in the range of 3 percent to 10 percent, commodities to which the 3 percent increase applied included fertilizers, sulphuric acid, anhydrous ammonia, and other bulk commodies which constitute major competitive waterborne movements. Thus some plants are located beside the river, not for water transportation, but for water competition. If it were not for the waterway, the intermodal competition would not be there. And neither would the plants.

Questionnaires are sometimes used to determine the influence of water transportation on river valley industrial development. If a questionnaire merely inquires as to the use of water transportation and its role as a factor in plant location, the results are bound to be fragmentary and misleading. More searching questions are required, looking into materials used by each plant, their origins, and the competitive character of charges by all modes.

A word of caution is likewise in order with respect to county-by-county studies. Do the counties bordering the navigable rivers, the Great Lakes, and the oceans experience a greater industrial growth than those inland? The findings of such studies can certainly be useful. But they must be read judiciously.

Every community on a navigable waterway is not equally favored. Industry tends to concentrate for access to diverse markets. As we have already noted, the water-based location is often at that point where rail and truck lines converge beside the navigable channel. Often the feasibility of long-distance transmission of electric energy or the proximity of pipeline connections proves a determinant. The availability of local resources may be crucial. Many, perhaps most, of the counties in the United States, both those inland and those on the waterways, lack these attractions, but with great variations in distribution as between those inland and those on the waters. In consequence, on some reaches of the waterways, there may be very little industrial development for many miles, while great concentrations appear at selected points. Inland, the same irregularity is manifest.

Studies which range the waterside counties of a particular state against the inland counties of that state are tempting but risky. The respective county groupings often have little com-

▲ Fiberglas reinforced underground storage tanks being loaded for a trip from Pittsburgh to Houston. In addition to lower shipping costs, use of the waterways eliminates clearance problems and need for special road permits for the tanks, which are 9 to 30 feet in length and eight to 12 feet in diameter.

parability because the regions of the state are too heterogeneous. The State of Tennessee, for example, comprises three large but very dissimilar regions: Eastern Mountain, Central Basin, and Western Slope and Delta—the State of Minnesota of at least four regions dissimilar in their economic base—and examples could be multiplied. Thus the distribution of resources, markets, and intermodal connections within a state is highly irregular. The more enlightening comparison will be that in which counties are grouped by the similarity of these attributes.

The clincher would seem to be the growth in employment, particularly in manufacturing. This gets directly at the income effect. Assuming a homogeneous grouping of counties, would not the growth of manufacturing jobs in waterside counties be the acid test? No. It would be a useful test, but a fragmentary one.

Water transportation buoys up jobs and incomes far inland as well as on the river bank. For example, the Twin Cities area of Minnesota, at the head of Mississippi River navigation, originated 1.6 million bushels of grain shipments by barge in 1946, 26.5 million bushels in 1956, and 155.3 million bushels in 1971. Most of this grain went to the Gulf Coast for export. It had been assembled at Twin Cities barging terminals from farms in at least five different states where its farm value in 1971 was over $200 million. Obviously, statistics on employment in counties on navigable water in Minnesota would have had little relevance to the impact on farm income dispersed throughout scores of counties far from the river.

The Minnesota grain movement is not unique in its inland impact. The poultry-feeding industry of the inland counties of Georgia and the Carolinas receives large quantities of waterborne feed grains by truck from Tennessee River ports, not to mention the tonnages received by rail at water-competitive rates. Since the institution of sharply reduced multiple-car railroad rates on grain movements to the Southeast in 1963, the waterborne movement from the Mississippi Valley via the Tennessee River has been recovering smartly, and in 1971 had again soared to 2.7 million tons.

Bituminous coal is another illustration of the effect on inland communities. Coal is carried by rail to barge-loading terminals on the Ohio River from West Virginia mines as far inland as 60 miles and a comparable distance to the Mississippi River from inland counties in Southern Illinois. As another illustration, electric utilities throughout the valleys of the Mississippi, Ohio, and Illinois Rivers, and as far away as Florida, transmit the benefits of waterborne coal to consuming communities far inland by high voltage transmission lines. Many instances could doubtlessly be found of particular inland communities in which the benefits of water transportation equal or exceed those bestowed on selected waterside counties.

Statistics as to numbers of persons employed are likewise limited because they make inadequate allowance for compensation differentials. A number of the industries which have expanded in greatest magnitude at waterway sites, and which are big waterway shippers, do not employ large numbers of persons. But, they do employ very high-salaried persons. This is characteristic, for example, of petroleum refining, chemical plants and electric utilities, with their staffs of scientists, engineers, and technicians. The income effect is thus disproportionately greater than the employment expansion. Furthermore, the higher levels of individual income exert an intangible, but highly constructive, influence on cultural, recreational, and other environmental features of the affected communities.

Probably the central problem in all economic studies of the local or regional employment income effect of waterway transportation is that these studies seek to measure growth at water-based locations versus growth at other locations. But this is not the real question. The real question is rather the income effect at water-based locations as it actually is versus what it would have been in the absence of the waterway. Suppose, for example, that the Pittsburgh district steel industry is not as buoyant as that of Chicago. But the Pittsburgh steel industry, if it were robbed of its enormous receipt of waterborne coal via the Monongahela and Ohio Rivers, would probably be only a fragment of its present structure.

Much of the expansive influence of water transportation is exerted on depressed regions, such as the Tennessee Valley and Appalachia. Jobs and incomes in these areas have long been sagging, and, in spite of the advantages of water transportation, they do not make a good showing against California and New Jersey. But without water transportation, the depressed regions would have fallen into a state of disastrous collapse. Thus in this field, as elsewhere, the economist is faced with his universal problem, not easily solvable by statistical measure—the problem of what would have happened under other conditions.

Stripped of all its technicalities, the stimulus of low-cost water transportation to industrial development and agricultural prosperity is clear and striking. The enormous growth in waterborne carriage of basic materials, fuels, and foodstuffs concurrently with expansion of the shipping and receiving industries at water-based locations is eloquent testimony. These industries, in turn, generate growth in supporting and satellite industries, and the community benefits extend far inland from the waterways.

Waterway Transportation and Natural Resources for a Growing Economy

In recent years, the doctrine of Dr. Malthus has become the subject of renewed and anxious attention. Will our natural resource base prove adequate to sustain the expanding U. S. population and the mounting national product this population will demand? Transportation on the inland waterways possesses a distinctive capability towards providing an affirmative answer to this question.

Transportation is production—preeminently so in the haulage of raw natural resource products. The waterways stand alone as specialized movers of diverse dry and liquid bulk resources. Most of the tonnage carried on the rivers and lakes consists of newly extracted minerals and crops, either in raw form or only initially processed. The sound development of the natural resource base of the mushrooming American economy thus calls for the fullest development of the efficiency potentials of this mode.

Ever more people at ever-rising standards of living are putting a strain on the country's reserves of natural resources. The United States began the 1970's with a population of 205 million. On low-growth assumptions, the Bureau of the Census projects a U. S. population in 1990 of over 260 million, an increment equivalent to the entire population of Great Britain. Natural resource extraction, of course, will mount even faster because of rising per-capita consumption. A recent study by Resources for the Future delineates the outlook for the year 2000. Even with the development of hydro and nuclear power, the consumption of fossil fuels measured in BTU's is projected at 170 percent of 1970. In 1970, we consumed 138 million net tons of iron ore. The outlook for 2000 calls for 341 million net tons. Associated projections foresee an output of textile fibers at 181 percent of the 1970 level, of commercial fertilizer at 244 percent, and of timber at 237 percent.

New technologies will expand the natural resource base. Will they expand it enough? No one knows. Oil may be obtained from shale—magnesium and other minerals from the oceans. Desalination of sea water will aid the coastal regions. Our soil resources are being greatly augmented by the application of chemical fertilizers. Here, too, water transportation plays a central role. Large and growing sectors of the fertilizer industry, along with other chemical production, are oriented to a water transport base.

The pressures on natural resources will mean resorting to ever-leaner sources, ever more remote from consuming populations. The attendant sacrifices of productive efficiency in extraction and processing can be substantially offset by rising efficiency of haulage. This is the task for water transportation.

Water transportation is the lowest-cost mode for a variety of large volume dry and liquid bulk movements. Bituminous coal provides a suitable example. The Interstate Commerce Commission reports that, in 1969, the average rail revenue on bituminous coal in the United States was 12.1 mills per ton-mile. Charges for coal transportation in the inland rivers, at about 3.0 mills per ton-mile, and on the lakes and oceans at some 2.0 mills or less, obviously fall well below the rail level.

The special role of water transportation in the logistics of natural resources is strikingly evident in the waterborne

Commodity Composition—U. S. Domestic Waterborne Commerce, 1971

	Percentage Carried Internal (On Rivers & Canals)	Percentage Carried (Including Coastwise & Lakewise)
Principally Raw Materials:		
Bituminous Coal	21.9	14.8
Non-Metallic Minerals (Ex. Fuels)	16.5	14.7
Crude Petroleum	11.7	12.1
Metallic Ores	1.1	7.5
Lumber & Wood Products	3.6	2.5
Marine Products	3.9	2.2
Farm Products	5.3	3.0
Sub-Totals	64.0	56.8
Principally Processed Products:		
Petroleum Products	21.8	32.0
Chemicals & Related Products	6.2	4.4
Sub-Totals	28.0	36.4
Other Commodities	8.0	6.8
Totals	100.0	100.0

SOURCE: U. S. Dept. of the Army, Corps of Engineers

commodity composition. This is shown in the table above. It will be noted that, in 1971, 64.0 percent of the tonnage carried by shallow-draft barging consisted of direct minerals and farm products. The inclusion of petroleum products and chemicals brings the total to 92.0 percent. For shallow-draft and deep-draft carriage combined, the corresponding percentages are 56.8 and 93.2. Clearly, the waterways may be viewed principally as a bridge system between the sites of domestic mineral and soil resources and distant consuming markets.

The importance of water transportation to natural resource production is not to be measured exclusively by the waterborne tonnages. In addition, water competition holds down railroad rates on the products of soils and mineral wealth. A wide variety of major bulk commodity movements are carried by rail at rates held at low levels by water competition. These apply to fertilizer materials, chemicals, coal, notably in the case of unit trains, and numerous other commodities. The low rates on grains to the Southeast, to the Gulf Coast, and to Pacific ports in the Columbia River Valley are famous examples. Indeed, rail rates from the Middle West to the Atlantic Coast are anchored to waterway competition. Waterway competition thus draws the railroads into a somewhat unwilling partnership in serving the nation's natural resource base.

Because of its strict cost orientation, water carriage is 100 percent economic production. Waterborne cargo is almost exclusively that of standardized commodities. Shippers determine origins, destinations, service requirements, and shipment quantities with sharpened pencils on a strict cost basis. In their specialized role as carriers of natural resource products, therefore, the waterways are an essential segment of natural resource production. They move minerals and crops from the surplus producing areas where prices are low to the deficiency areas where prices, in the absence of waterway transportation, would be drastically higher, thus holding the price differential to the narrow spread consisting of barging and handling costs. In the economic sense, the waterways are thus a segment of the natural resource production system.

The water transport contribution is especially vital because of the great distances to be traversed. Nature has placed rich mineral and soil resources far away from the major consuming populations. In a continental economy, resort to the richest resources necessarily demands the bridging of great distances. The contribution of low-cost water transportation is thus crucial to resource development.

In its natural resources role, water transportation helps restrain the tendency for the United States to become a "have-not" nation—a nation too dependent on foreign sources for essential materials and fuels.

In the petroleum industry, water carriage complements pipelines in sustaining domestic production. Petroleum barging provides a necessary flexibility, which pipelines lack, in handling smaller-lot movement and in redirecting the flow in response to changing markets and seasons. The barges and tankers are thus an indispensable segment of the logistical system, especially between the Gulf Coast and the huge markets of the Northeast in the face of competition with oil imports from overseas.

In the years following World War II, it appeared that the United States was to become a conspicuously "have-not" nation with respect to domestic iron ore reserves. The traditional direct shipping ores of the Lake Superior district were rapidly being depleted and the end of their availability came in sight.

The "have-not" outlook has, in a limited measure, been fulfilled by a rising dependence on imported ores. From 1950 to 1971, iron ore imports grew from 7.7 percent to 33.9 percent of the U. S. supply. Meanwhile, however, a new domestic resource had been developed—the previously useless "taconites" and "jaspers"—made usable by new technologies for converting these minerals into high-grade concentrates. On the basis of these technologies, the American mining industry has been investing hundreds of millions of dollars in new plants, principally in the Lake Superior district, to concentrate and agglomerate the crude minerals, thus effectively stemming the "have-not" tide.

The new concentrating industry is too far from its major domestic markets, particularly the steel districts of Pittsburgh, Youngstown, and the Lake Erie shore, to have grown on any but a water transport base. By rail, Duluth is 792 miles from Cleveland, 920 miles from Pittsburgh, too far to compete with foreign ores received via the Atlantic Coast. Lake transportation is the obvious salvation of this natural resource problem.

With iron ore concentrates valued in the neighborhood of $12.50 per gross ton in the Lake Superior producing district, it is obvious that the water-based development of this industry has made a valuable contribution to the balance of international payments. This contribution combines with that of the carriage of finished steel on the inland rivers to markets on the Gulf Coast and in the Mississippi Valley where foreign competition is very strong. In 1971, 3.1 million tons of finished steel were shipped by river barges from Ohio Valley mills, principally from the Pittsburgh district, the greater portion to Mississippi Valley and Gulf Coast destinations. With Gulf Coast imports falling in the range of 3 to 4 million tons annually, most of the water shipments supplant a corresponding tonnage of imported steel.

Water transportation is likewise a stimulus to exports. In 1971, for example, 594 million bushels of grains and soybeans, originating as far inland as Kansas, Minnesota, and Illinois, were received by river barges at Gulf Coast ports, principally for export.

Paradoxically, while the economy of the United States strains at its natural resource base, major specialized producing regions suffer inadequate incomes. The low cost of moving the products of these regions by water provides substantial relief. Until the development of taconite processing, the mining regions of the Lake Superior district were confronted with stagnation. Appalachian coal is carried by water to markets as distant as Tampa, Florida, in keen competition with foreign and domestic oil and gas. Grain farming in the Upper Mississippi Basin and the Pacific Northwest benefits not only from low-cost access to distant markets, but, in addition, by the waterborne receipt of chemical fertilizers, tractor fuel, and other essential fuels and products. In the Southeast, poultry and animal feeding are sustained by waterborne grains via the Mississippi and Tennessee Rivers. The development of the water transport connections for these and other regions producing minerals and crops is clearly essential to any effective program of regional improvement in employment and incomes.

Water transportation is an integral segment of natural resource development. This is especially true of multipurpose water resource projects in which navigation is a feature. Depending on the particular river basin program, navigation potential is commonly a significant joint product of other water resource objectives, and, in many instances, the prospective contribution of navigation is an essential element in overall project justification.

Full utilization of the potentials of domestic water transportation will thus continue to be a built-in feature of natural resource development and conservation. Not only is water transportation the one mode peculiarly specialized in its logistical role as a carrier of natural resources; it is, in itself, to a substantial degree, a joint product of other objectives in our water resource development program. It will have much to do with reducing our preoccupation with the doctrine of Thomas Malthus in the generation ahead.

The Transportation Bargain

The water carriers of the United States are giving the American consumer an ever more attractive bargain. In a period of general inflation, the costs of transportation by water remain low. From 1964 to 1972, the U. S. consumer price index soared upward by 34.2 percent. But, during this same period, the average charge for shallow-draft inland water transportation edged downward from 3.5 to 3.3 mills per ton-mile. (A mill is 1/10 of a cent.) By way of comparison, average railroad charges in 1971 were 15.9 mills per ton-mile, nearly five times as high.

Low-cost water carriage has been a principal influence in restraining railroad rate increases on commodities adapted to water transportation. From 1958 to 1964, the average revenue per ton-mile carried by the railroads went down by 12 percent, and in 1972 was still only 10 percent above the 1958 level. Waterway competition has been an important contributor to this record, particularly as it affects rates on those bulk commodities most pervasive in their influence on living costs—farm products, fuels, chemicals, primary metals, and the like.

Nor has this restraining influence been a cause of unsatisfactory railroad earnings. Waterway competition has spurred the railroads in the introduction of cost-cutting technologies—for example, the unit train, the aluminum closed-top hopper car, and multiple-car shipments. Railroad executives have repeatedly emphasized the profitability of these water-competitive innovations.

For many years prior to the 1960's, it was an accepted rule of thumb that the average charge for shallow-draft water carriage was about 4.0 mills per ton-mile. By 1972, however, this had declined to the 3.3 mills reported by the Interstate Commerce Commission. This reporting applies only to the ICC-regulated carriers who carry substantial tonnages of non-bulk freight necessitating higher costs and rates. The overall average, including all the lower-rated bulk commodity movements, as well, would run somewhat lower.

Important examples of non-regulated bulk commodity movements include petroleum and petroleum products. These comprise about 33.4 percent of all inland waterway tonnage. The cost of some oil industry barging is now as low as 1¾ mills per ton-mile, including all overhead on power units, barges, and terminals. Short hauls of small lots can run up to 4 mills. But, giving weight to the dominant heavy tonnage, long-haul nature of the movement, petroleum executives generally confirm an average of about 2 mills per ton-mile.

◄ This powerful towboat bucks river current at four to five miles an hour.

Bituminous coal is another 22.0 percent of shallow-draft waterborne tonnage. Mining executives and electric utility consumers offer an estimate of 3 mills per ton-mile as the average cost of coal barging. Where a good balancing of two-way movements can be obtained, costs on dry bulk movements run even lower. For example, much of the southbound grain movement on the Mississippi River for export is balanced by northbound return hauls of ores, fertilizer, and salt. The resulting high level of equipment and labor utilization has reduced the cost of long-haul barging of grain and soybeans to the range of 2½ to 2¾ mills per ton-mile. Rates on northbound fertilizer and fertilizer materials run even lower than this at 2 to 2½ mills. While some shorthaul waterborne movements in small lots call for charges as high as 7 mills, the present average, weighted for ton-mileage of volume, is now probably close to 3 mills.

Competitive railroad charges reflect the influence of these low rates. The Mississippi River barging charge on grains and soybeans from the upper Midwest to the Gulf Coast averages about 14 cents a bushel. The latest reported average rail charge on wheat from Kansas to Louisiana was 17.6 cents a bushel, competitive with the Missouri-Mississippi River route. In competition with the Illinois-Mississippi River route, the rail charge on corn from Illinois to Louisiana averaged 10.9 cents a bushel.

Railroad unit train rates on coal, iron ore, and other minerals are commonly a response to waterway competition. The unit train carriage of utility coal from Percy to Plaines, Illinois, was instituted at a rate of only 5 mills per ton-mile in direct competition with barge movement on the Illinois River. By comparison, the non-water-competitive unit train movement of utility coal to Cleveland, Ohio, was concurrently yielding the railroads a revenue of 16.6 mills per ton-mile.

The competition-induced unit train is good for the railroads. The Association of American Railroads says: "Though the unit train concept is simple, it did not come into general use until after 1960. Its growth has been a factor in the railroads' partial recovery from a near-disastrous 1.97 percent rate of return on net investment in 1961 . . ." The role of the waterways in bringing down railroad charges via the unit train technology would thus appear a benefit to the railroads themselves.

The table on the following page is a sample, which could be multiplied many times, of the restraining effect of waterway competition on railroad rates.

Low barging costs and water-induced reductions in railroad rates might seem to constitute a discrimination against those communities not located on navigable waters. However, the development of truck feeder service, of pipeline connections, and of long-distance transmission of electricity communicates the benefits of water carriage far inland. Wheat carried by barge down the Mississippi River originates as far inland as North Dakota. The introduction of trucking service from the inland community of Garden City, Kansas, to Missouri River elevators at Kansas City induced a rail rate reduction from $17.20 to $11.70 per ton on export wheat from Garden City to New Orleans. Electric energy generated on the riverbank from waterborne coal is being transmitted ever-longer distances inland by high-voltage transmission lines.

Thus, the benefits of water transportation reach most of the population of the country. About 94 percent of the American people reside in states which are served by water carriage. Cross-state highways, pipelines, and electric lines convey the advantages of water

Railroad Charges on Water-Adapted Movements
Water-Competitive Compared with Non-Water-Competitive

	Rail Distance (Miles)	Railroad Charge per Ton: Water Competitive	Railroad Charge per Ton: Non-Water Competitive
Export Wheat to New Orleans:			
From St. Louis	685	$ 5.30	
From Oklahoma City	673		$ 8.00
Export Grain to Portland, Oregon:			
From Connell, Washington	325	3.70	
From Medford, Oregon	329		9.60
Phosphate Rock for Fertilizer:			
From Tampa, Florida:			
To Norfolk, Virginia	802	4.95	
To Lynchburg, Virginia	781		7.40
Oyster Shells for Chicken Feed:			
From Houston, Texas:			
To Minneapolis	1,198	9.85	
To Cedar Rapids, Iowa	1,021		13.02
Bituminous Coal to Minneapolis:			
From West Frankfort, Ill.	619	3.37	
From Linton, Indiana	595		5.02
Structural Steel to St. Louis:			
From Pittsburgh, Penna.	604	10.00	
From Cleveland, Ohio	522		14.60

transportation to the larger portion of these communities.

For a wide variety of basic materials, fuels, and foodstuffs, inland waterway transportation is the lowest-cost mode of carriage. The rivers and canals are carrying large and growing tonnages of such commodities, a service of vital importance to widespread regions and industries. Costs remain stable, firmly resisting inflationary pressures, and the competitive restraint on railroad rate increases extends the benefits into all sectors of the economy. The American transportation bargain is, in very large measure, waterway-induced.

The High Productivity of Water Transport Investment

The rapid growth in the demand for freight transportation in the United States is straining every capital resource of the carriers. The stakes are very high. Success in expanding transport capability is essential to economic growth and to restraint of cost inflation.

Of the various surface modes, inland water transportation can expand the most for the least investment. But, this capability is contingent on an adequate and modernized navigation system. Taking into account public and private in-

Table I.

Investment Efficiency of Railway and Waterway Carrying Equipment

A. Railway Freight Cars Compared With Barges

	1. Ton-Miles Carried per Car or per Barge in Service 1970	2. Average Cost New per Car or per Barge Acquired 1970	3. Indicated Annual Ton-Miles per Dollar of New Investment (Col. 1 ÷ Col. 2)
Railway Freight Cars	523,048	$15,625	33.5
Barges	8,277,250	90,000	92.0

B. Diesel Locomotives Compared With Towboats

	1. Ton-Miles Propelled per Horse-power of Units in Service 1970	2. Average Cost per Horsepower of New Units Acquired 1970	3. Indicated Annual Ton-Miles per Dollar of new Investment (Col. 1 ÷ Col. 2)
Diesel Locomotives	15,365	$ 84.90	181.9
Towboats	55,342	275.00	201.2

SOURCES: Interstate Commerce Commission
U. S. Dept. of the Army, Corps of Engineers

vestment, combined, no other surface mode can match water transportation in conservation of capital.

The official records show that every dollar invested in a river barge accommodates an annual movement of 92 ton-miles of freight. Invested in a railway freight car, that dollar accommodates only 34 annual ton-miles.

Again, measuring river towboats against diesel locomotives in horsepower equivalents, one dollar invested in a towboat yields 201 ton-miles of yearly cargo propulsion. In a railway diesel locomotive, the dollar provides only 182 ton-miles. The data of this comparison appear in Table I.

The high productivity of water carrier investment reflects the strong dedication to high equipment utilization which characterizes the industry. Relevant policies include assignment to respective segments of the waterway system of barges and towboats most suited to operation on those segments, the associated development of interchange arrangements, and the design of both powered and cargo-carrying vessels for maximum service.

Big line-haul towboats, each representing an investment of $1.5 million or more, are kept moving in long-haul service. The break-up and assembly of large intercity tows and switching within harbor areas is left to smaller harbor boats. The individual towboat is systematically assigned to the type of service for which it is designed. For example, in a movement from New Orleans to Pittsburgh, the heavily-loaded tow moving upstream against the current of the Mississippi River as far as Cairo, Illinois, may be propelled by a 6,000-horsepower towboat, representing an investment of $2 million dollars. But, for the slack-water portion of the trip from Cairo to Pittsburgh, the tow is transferred to a smaller 3,200-horsepower unit costing some $300,000 less, conserving investment and achieving operating economies as well.

The rising volume of traffic expands the scope of such interchange. The entire logistical systems of groups of new shipping and receiving installations, at great distances from each other on the river system, are being constructed around planned interchange movements. This is true of an increasing number of operations in such industries as chemicals, electric utilities, petroleum refining and marketing, blast furnace operations, and farm product marketing. Movements on the Lower Mississippi interchange, not only at Cairo for movement on the Ohio, but also at St. Louis for the Missouri upstream to Omaha and Sioux City, at Alton for the Illinois Waterway into Chicago, and on the Upper Mississippi for points extending all the way to the Twin Cities.

The biggest single factor in investment efficiency on the inland waterways is probably the rising horsepower of towboats, associated with larger tonnages per tow. Attention has become focused on this development since the launching of the 9,000-horsepower *America* of the Federal Barge Lines. A growing portion of towboats in recent years has been in the higher horsepower ranges—typically 5,000 to 6,000. The increased capacity of a larger towboat is considerably greater than the differential investment. For example, a 5,000 horsepower towboat exceeds the propulsion capacity of a 3,200 horsepower vessel by 56 percent. But, one inland shipbuilder quotes a price on the larger of these two only 13 percent higher than on the smaller, and this is typical. Thus, with larger vessels, the investment per horsepower declines.

In addition to increased horsepower per towboat, each horsepower is moving more cargo. In 1961, an average of 32,482 ton-miles of freight were moved in internal waterborne commerce per horsepower of towboats in service. In the early 1970's, this had risen to over 40,000 ton-miles per horsepower. While the aggregate horsepower of all towboats in service went up by 44.4 percent, the cargo ton-miles hauled rose by 85.7 percent.

Various methods are employed to extend towboat service life. As towboats become obsolete, they are commonly rebuilt, repowered, and outfitted anew. Towboats which become obsolete on one river section are transferred to others. Modernization and extended service life thus go hand in hand.

Carriers extend the service life of barges by consigning aging vessels to secondary service. In primary service, for example, a barge might operate on the Lower Mississippi River where tows of 30 barges or more are not unusual. Maneuvering a large tow in the channels of the river imposes severe strains on the individual vessel in the tow, especially when fully loaded. After some years of such service, the barge is normally transferred to short haul service in the upper reaches of the tributaries where smaller tows are characteristic.

Another important contributor to investment conservation is the double-skinned barge. This design makes possible numerous backhaul arrangements as between commodities otherwise incompatible with each other, such as bituminous coal and grain. The hold formed by the inner skin, being free from structural members, may be quickly and completely cleaned, eliminating all residues of previous cargo. By rendering such backhauls feasible, the double-skinned barge reduces investment in vessels which otherwise would be returned empty.

The double-skinned barge adds further to service life by insulating the cargo from the effect of outer-hull abrasion and impact. Where considerations of cargo protection would sometimes counsel removal of a single-skinned barge from service, in the double-skinned barge the cargo remains secure from contamination. The double skin, especially of tank barges, is an important safety feature. In the event of impact damage to the outer hull, the inner skin protects the river water from pollution by leakage of liquid cargo. Inland shipbuilders report that the great majority of new tank barges are now being built with double skins.

Constantly increasing length of haul increases the service life of barges. In 1961, the average haul of internal waterborne freight was 286.7 miles. Rising, year by year, in the early 1970's, the average haul exceeded 330 miles. Wear and tear on barges is principally in loading and unloading, particularly from impact with shoreside equipment, such as clamshell buckets. Longer hauls reduce the amount of in-harbor activity relative to revenue ton-miles carried and lengthen barge life.

The effect of these circumstances shows up clearly in the record. The carriers have been hauling ever more freight per dollar invested. From 1964 to 1970, the ton-miles of cargo carried by the Classes A and B carriers by water increased by 42.5 percent. But, in spite of the rising costs of new vessel and terminal construction, their long-term investment rose only one-third as much—by 13.9 percent. Sharply rising efficiency in equipment utilization is reflected in this record.

It is clearly evident, therefore, that within a national program to expand the freight-carrying capacity of the multi-modal transportation network, policies conducive to modernization and enlargement of the navigation system must play a key role. The mounting demands upon the nation's supplies of capital are exceeding all previous experience. A modernized navigation system conducive to investment of private capital at the highest standards of transport productivity thus assumes in this era a position of top priority.

The Inland Waterways and American Agriculture

On inland waterway transportation, some economists take a hard line. In marginalist theory, all men are equal. For the same product all pay the same price—rich and poor alike. Similarly, these economists argue, all modes of transportation should be equal. As between waterways, railroads, and other modes, government expenditure and user charge policy should aim at equivalent standards of cost responsibility. Then, they say, let the modes fight it out on even competitive terms, and the consumer can choose.

But economic policy makes wide departures from marginalist theory. In economic policy, all men are not equal.

Take taxation, for example. On a hard Marshallian line, all citizens should pay taxes at the same percentage of income. But, very few economists, indeed, would go along with this.

As with taxes, marginal cost pricing will not explain public housing rent policy, aid to depressed areas, antitrust exemption for organized labor, aid to agriculture, urban renewal, or numerous other policy applications. Hard line marginalism, likewise, would be a poor base for inland water transport policy.

Inland waterborne commerce in the United States has been developed on a distinctive pattern directly serving vital sectors of public interest. For example, on the 1,500 miles of navigable Appalachian rivers, water transportation has given immense support to an otherwise sagging economy. The waterways are proving an essential medium in contending with the energy crisis. They carry enormous volumes of coal and petroleum fuels to regions of scarcity. Most inland waterway commerce serves the previously retarded, but now rapidly progressing, industrial economy of the South. The contribution of waterway transportation to American agriculture in an era of mounting world-wide demand for foodstuffs is so important that it deserves detailed attention.

Farm incomes are directly dependent on low-cost transportation to market. Farming is a geographically dispersed industry, and the rich farm lands of the interior are remote from the major coastal populations. As an export industry, agriculture must move its products over continental distances to seaports. And, the foreign buyer's demand for U. S. farm products, as opposed to those of other nations, is very price-elastic. Therefore, any saving in overland transportation cost is bestowed principally on the American farmer. Farm products have a low value per ton so that transport cost is a large portion of delivered price.

The waterways, as carriers of large volume, bulk commodities, are ideal for farm crops, moving them at a cost averaging only about 3 mills per ton-mile.

U. S. waterway policy, from its earliest origins, has been deeply concerned with farming. For example, the extensive navigation improvements of the Upper Mississippi, the Tennessee, and the Illinois Rivers were justified, in large measure, by what they would do for farming.

Herbert Hoover, speaking as Secretary of Commerce in 1927, and pushing for waterway improvement, was voicing a widely-held preoccupation when he said:

> "I believe that the statement often made that by the modernization of the Mississippi and the Great Lakes system of waterways we shall decrease the freight on grain to the world markets by 10 cents a bushel is not far wrong.
>
> "And by so doing we should increase the price for all grain to the farmer by 10 cents per bushel, and this 10 cents is the profit end of the price. One single year of such increase to our midwest farmers would more than equal the entire capital outlay which we propose."

Let's look at the magnitude of waterborne farm crop movements. In 1971, shallow-draft barging carried 879.6 million bushels of farm crops. These had an approximate farm value of $1.5 billion. Over 51.7 million bushels of wheat, barley, and rye were carried in domestic waterborne commerce on the Columbia River. (This excludes coastwise movements.)

Of course, the big, arterial movement is that of the Mississippi River and its tributaries. In 1971, the Upper Mississippi, the Missouri, and the Illinois Rivers originated 651.5 million bushels of corn, wheat, soybeans, and other crops, with a farm value exceeding $1 billion.

The wheat originated on the Missouri, Upper Mississippi, and Illinois Rivers in 1971 was equivalent to 70 percent of the 1971 wheat harvest of the entire state of Nebraska. The corn was equivalent to 35 percent of all the corn harvested in Illinois, including that kept on Illinois farms for animal feed.

The farm benefits extend far inland. Grain is hauled by rail and truck to river ports from all parts of Minnesota, Wisconsin, Iowa, and Illinois, as well as from North Dakota and Wyoming. Kansas City grain originates principally in Kansas and Nebraska. Farm crops are hauled from the interior of Indiana and Kentucky to Ohio River ports.

A big portion of the farm crop movement serves animal and poultry feeding in the Southeast.

In 1971, 95.6 million bushels were terminated at Tennessee River ports, including 43.4 million at Guntersville, Alabama, and 37.6 million at Chattanooga. These grains are distributed, principally by truck, throughout the Carolinas, Georgia, and Alabama. Thus, the river system furnishes an economic channel between two great farm regions, the Upper Midwest and the Southeast.

Water carriage provides a competitive base for railroad rates. Water transportation is inherently competitive, characterized by ease of entry and small scale of the individual firm. By contrast, on any particular railroad movement, in the absence of waterway competition, rates would be inherently a product of oligopoly pricing. With progressive merging of the railroads, on many directional movements, the oligopoly is becoming monopoly, reinforced by conference rate making under the Reed-Bulwinkle policy.

Trucking competition is mostly for short and intermediate hauls. The trucking movement gets competitively weak on long hauls, such as Kansas City to Chattanooga or Burlington to New Orleans. And these are the movements which make or break the farmer. This is clearly indicated in Table I.

On long hauls which are not water-competitive, truck competition has not brought rail rates down. But, waterway competition has.

Without the inherently competitive low-cost barging on the inland waterways, the inland farming basins of the Upper Midwest and, also, those of northern Idaho and eastern Oregon and Washington would undergo the slow strangulation of noncompetitive railroad rate setting.

Waterborne movements inbound to farm areas are also important. Fertilizer materials and products reach the farm over very long distances. The main source of phosphates is Florida. Most ammonia, sulphur, and sulphuric acid comes from the Gulf Coast or the Upper Tennessee and Ohio Rivers. These are low-valued, large-volume, bulk materials, like farm crops, for which water carriage is well suited and for which transportation cost is vital.

In 1971, 2.3 million tons of fertilizer and fertilizer materials were brought by barge from southern origins into the farming areas of the Upper Midwest. This averages out at about 4.8 tons per farm in the four states of Iowa, Minnesota, Wisconsin, and Illinois. The tonnages delivered by rail at low, water-competitive rates are correspondingly big.

In modern farming, tractor fuel, gasoline for trucks, and fuel oil have become major cost elements. Petroleum product barging, "the poor man's pipeline,"

Table I

Railroad Charges on Farm Products
Water-Competitive Compared with Non-Water-Competitive

	Rail Distance (Miles)	Railroad Charge per Ton: Water-Competitive	Railroad Charge per Ton: Non-Water-Competitive
Export Wheat to New Orleans:			
From St. Louis	685	$ 5.30	
From Oklahoma City	673		$ 8.00
Export Grain to Portland, Oregon:			
From Connell, Washington	325	3.70	
From Medford, Oregon	329		9.60
Wheat for Export:			
St. Louis to New Orleans	685	5.30	
Amarillo to Houston	596		8.00
Corn for Export:			
Chicago to New Orleans	890	7.50	
Ottumwa, Iowa to New Orleans	932		11.40
Corn for Poultry Feeding:			
St. Louis to Chattanooga	654	4.17	
Buffalo to Augusta, Maine	606		8.60

serves the small, independent product distributors, contributing to low prices. Farm cooperatives, themselves, carry on a significant volume of petroleum product barging. Petroleum products, of course, are among the largest tonnage barge receipts in such river districts as the Upper Mississippi and the Columbia.

Inbound movements of bituminous coal for electric utilities also benefit farming. The modern farm is a big electricity consumer, not only for powered machinery, but for refrigeration and illumination of large working structures and open yards. In 1971, 8.3 million tons of coal were delivered by barge on the Upper Mississippi and Illinois Rivers. Long distance transmission carries electric energy to farm areas far inland from the riverbank.

As with aid to Appalachia, American public policy is now directed towards a multi-faceted and costly program of aid to agriculture. Over the long term, the encouragement of water transportation has played an important role in this program. As Herbert Hoover indicated in 1927, the depressed condition of agriculture was a dominant consideration in the improvement of the Upper Mississippi and Illinois Rivers, pressed to completion in the late 1930's. American agriculture still is not in good shape. Its condition could become critical again.

The rigid application of hard-line marginal cost principles to the waterways, whether in the area of competitive rate regulation or the imposition of user charges, would fall with a differentially severe impact on farming, defeating a central purpose of major waterway improvements and frustrating farm policy. We trust that most will agree that the public policy objective should be governing.

Waterway Modernization for an Expanding Economy

The view is sometimes expressed that freight transportation is playing a declining role in the American economy. The decentralization of industry, it is held, puts the producer closer to the consumer so products don't have to be hauled so far. This is a naive conception. All production of movable commodities begins with the extractive industries at the raw materials source—the mineral deposits, farms, forests, and seacoast fisheries—and has to be moved, in one form or another, to the centers of the consuming populations.

Progressive urbanization is concentrating the masses of consumers even farther from resources. And principal resource origins are either remaining where they have always been or, with depletion of existing deposits, coming from new origins farther away. "Oil is where you find it." And, it has been found in large volume in such regions as the North Slope of Alaska.

The decline in average freight charges, along with improvements in service, also tends to enlarge the role of freight transportation. In locating new plants and distributing orders geographically, the entrepreneur makes a trade-off between localities high in on-site costs but with short freight hauls, and localities low in on-site costs but requiring long freight hauls. The prices of on-site production factors, especially labor, have been going up more than freight rates. Geographical shifts in production, calling for longer hauls, follow. The demand schedule for freight transportation is a normal one—a lower price, relative to the alternatives, substantially expands the quantities taken by the customer.

Inland water carriage has been the bellwether in holding down freight costs. Since the late 1950's the average charge for inland water carriage has gone down from about 4 mills per ton-mile to some 3 mills. Influenced by this and other competitive inducements, the average rail charge has been held in check, changing from 1.445 cents per ton-mile in 1959 to 1.594 cents in 1971. In both of these modes, and very conspicuously also in highway trucking, service has been improved. As one measure of the consequence, from 1952 through 1972, the records of The American Waterways Operators, Inc., show the construction or expansion of 8,742 plants, terminals, industrials parks, and port districts at water-oriented locations.

We should expect, therefore, that the demand for freight transportation will go up about as fast as the real national product. We would say faster but for the growing element of services in the overall product. The ton-miles of internal waterborne domestic commerce carried yearly have been reported only since 1961. As shown in Table I, they have been going up faster than the real national product.

The growth in waterborne ton-miles carried per $100 of real GNP is a record of eleven years. But, in the interest of conservatism, let us assume that inland waterborne freight will continue to bear only the same relationship to real GNP between now and 1985 that it bore in 1971, namely, 15.4 ton-miles per $100 GNP. This gives us the expectation shown in Table II.

Table I

Internal Domestic Waterborne Ton-Miles Carried Compared with Real Gross National Product

Year	GNP in 1971 dollars (Billions)	Internal Waterborne Ton-Miles Carried	
		Aggregate (Billions)	Per $100 of GNP (In 1971 Dollars)
1961	$ 704.3	84.3	12.0
1962	750.6	89.6	11.9
1963	780.3	94.4	12.1
1964	823.0	101.9	12.4
1965	873.4	109.7	12.6
1966	924.2	117.3	12.7
1967	956.2	128.3	13.4
1968	1,000.7	139.3	13.9
1969	1,027.6	144.0	14.0
1970	1,022.6	155.8	15.2
1971	1,050.4	161.3	15.4

SOURCES: Board of Governors of the Federal Reserve System;
U. S. Dept. of the Army, Corps of Engineers

Table II.

Real Gross National Product and Internal Waterborne Ton-Miles Projected to 1975, 1980, and 1985

(At 15.4 Ton-Miles per $100 GNP)

Years	GNP in 1971 Dollars (Billions)	Internal Waterborne Ton-Miles (Billions)
1970	$1,022.6	155.8
1971	1,050.4	161.3
1975	1,317.3	202.9
1980	1,602.7	246.8
1985	1,949.9	300.3

The projection of Table II indicates an increase by 1985 of 86 percent over 1971. But, this immense growth, so essential to the national economy, can occur only with an adequate modernization of the U. S. navigation system. Modern and highly sophisticated vessel units are becoming progressively hampered in obsolete harbor and channel installations, many of them constructed 40 to 50 years ago. The economy's water transportation requirements of 1985 can be met only within the framework of a navigation system designed to the dimensions of those requirements.

A prominent public official recently commented that "the demands we will be making upon the transportation system in the next few years could bring it to the point of collapse." In certain arterial interchange sections of the U. S. inland waterway system the "point of collapse" is virtually at hand. One of these sections includes Lock No. 26 on the Mississippi River at Alton, Illinois, just below the mouth of the Illinois River.

This lock lies between the Upper Mississippi River Basin, including the Illinois River and Waterway, and the entire lower basin and the Gulf Coast. Much of the cargo moving through it originates and terminates at points as far away as Houston, New Orleans, and Mobile to the south, Pittsburgh to the east, Chicago and Minneapolis to the north, and to the west, Omaha and Kansas City. In short, Lock No. 26 lies at the central crossroads of the U. S. inland waterway system.

Expeditious progress in replacing Lock No. 26 is of the highest urgency. At an earlier date, responsible engineering studies placed its economic cargo-moving capacity at 41.0 million tons per year. In 1938, the year it was opened, Lock No. 26 transited 1.4 million tons; in 1959 this had risen to 21.0 million tons. In 1972, nearly 47.0 million tons of freight wormed their way through Lock No. 26, and not much more could get through. Replacement facilities will require several years to complete, and, until they are opened to service, this critical reach of the Mississippi River will remain an obstacle to expanded production and sustained efficiency in basic industries throughout the central regions of the country and the Gulf Coast.

Similar crises may be anticipated—and, if timely action is taken, averted—in other arterial reaches of the system. The Lower Ohio River, for example, constitutes the central interchange between four river systems, the Cumberland, the Tennessee, the Ohio, and the Mississippi. The chronic and costly bottleneck of old navigation structures in this reach were in process of replacement by temporary facilities in the early 1970's. But, in a few years, the temporary structures will become progressively less reliable and, in time, inadequate. Prompt action is required if these, too, are not to join Lock No. 26 as barriers to growth and efficiency in those broad sectors of industry and agriculture dependent on low-cost water transportation.

Additional inadequacies in the navigation system may be cited. Traffic tonnage through the lock of the Inner Harbor Navigation Canal in New Orleans has reached the threshold of physical capacity. Until this lock is replaced or supplemented, it must become an insuperable barrier to traffic growth between the eastern Gulf Coast and all the waterway reaches west and north of New Orleans.

A growing portion of the Illinois River system—the only existing waterway connection between the Mississippi River and the Great Lakes-St. Lawrence Seaway—is now carrying traffic at close to its economic capacity. On the Mississippi, replacement of Lock No. 27 approaches an urgency comparable to that of Lock No. 26. Certain old locks on the system are in danger of collapse. Inter-basin connections between existing waterways would expedite the flow of commerce. Inadequacies could be cited for the Columbia Basin, the Gulf Intracoastal, the Atlantic Intracoastal and others.

Public policy with respect to the water transport requirements of the coming decades may take either of two directions. Policy may become restrictive. We have noted that the large and growing demand for freight carriage by water and other modes constitutes, in part, a response to the decline in charges. By raising costs and charges, demand growth might be stunted to fit the limited capacity of the system. Such a policy might include the imposition of user charges on the waterways, an imposed scarcity policy sometimes advocated as a device for rationing limited capacity. It could include restrictive standards for economic justification of proposed navigation projects. With costs and rates high, and capacity low, the public would be constrained to buy less transportation. Consumers could purchase goods produced less efficiently but nearer their homes. Producers could confine their selling efforts more exclusively to local markets, limiting output accordingly.

The alternative policy is to expand the transportation system in step with the growing economy and without innovative restrictions on demand. We believe that most will concur with this policy. The consumers who are served include food buyers on the Atlantic Coast, purchasing meats and poultry from the Southeast produced from waterborne feed crops grown in the Middle West. They include Appalachian motorists and farmers buying low-cost waterborne gasoline. They comprise, also, householders on the Gulf Coast whose electricity bills are lower by virtue of waterborne coal. Producers whose growing output is carried by water include the Kentucky coal miners whose production is shipped to the Gulf Coast utilities and the farmers of the Upper Midwest whose crops in ever-rising volumes are carried, not only to the Southeast, but to the Gulf Coast for export. Examples could be multiplied.

Every consideration of public policy counsels a sustained expansion of the transportation system to keep it in pace with the expanding economy. The U. S. balance of payments is affected by massive quantities of farm crops shipped via the waterways to the coasts for export and on waterborne movements of steel, bituminous coal, and other commodities to coastal markets in competition with imports. The economic strength of hitherto underdeveloped regions of the country is involved—the Appalachian Region, the Tennessee Valley, the Southeast, the Arkansas Basin, and sub-areas of the Upper Middlewestern farm region. As a major carrier of fuels, water transportation plays a key role in contending with the emerging energy crisis. Modern navigation works are joint undertakings with water-based recreational sites, flood control works, improved water supply systems, and a variety of other water resource functions.

Our estimate of an 86 percent increase in the volume of water transportation by 1985 is a conservative one. The volume could well double. But, this vital target can be attained only on the basis of a modernization program of dimensions adequate to the challenge.

Inland Shipbuilding for the Exacting Standards of the Rivers

Certain American industries are small in scale but crucial to the efficiency of numerous other industries, vastly exceeding them in size, but dependent on these little giants for essential equipment. Among these we would have to number, for example, the manufacturer of ball and roller bearings and of machine tools. We should most emphatically have to include the inland shipbuilding industry. The industry designs and builds barges, towboats, and maintenance vessels for the inland waterways.

For the sake of simplicity we shall refer to barge and towboat construction as the "inland shipbuilding" industry, although some of it is on the coasts. Certain coastal shipyards, especially on the Gulf and the Atlantic, build principally oceangoing ships, but construct also shallow-draft vessels for the sheltered intracoastal waterways. But, much of the industry is truly inland, located in such centers as Pittsburgh, Louisville, St. Louis, and Nashville. Surprisingly, some of these interior shipyards build a few oceangoing ships, too, to be floated for hundreds of miles down the rivers for service at sea.

The indirect contribution of this small industry to the general economy is very great. Major American industries owe much of their efficiency to the low cost of obtaining essential materials and fuels over long distances by barge. Some big industries also reach important markets, otherwise inaccessible, by this means. Coal mining, steel, chemicals, oil refining, electric energy and the marketing of farm crops are among the water-based industries. Aluminum reduction depends on the availability of low-cost electric energy, often produced from waterborne fuels.

For commodities which can be moved in large tonnages and not requiring precision scheduling, water carriage provides transportation for only a fraction of the charges of any other surface mode. For example, the average railroad revenue per ton-mile on coal at the beginning of the 1970's exceeded 12 mills, in contrast to less than 3.0 mills charged by the barge lines. Similar comparisons would apply to petroleum products, chemicals, metallic ores, crushed stone, and a wide variety of other high tonnage commodities. For this reason, a very large sector of American industry, with annual sales in the billions of dollars, has developed, both for transportation and water supply, at water-based locations and built its logistical system on low-cost barge transportation.

Much of the efficiency of barge transportation, in turn, is attributable to aggressive innovation in the design of floating equipment. Over the past 15 years, in the face of rather drastic price inflation elsewhere in the economy, the average charge for barge transportation has gone down about 25 percent, from 4 mills to 3 mills per ton-mile. With sharply higher costs, especially higher labor rates, this achievement has been possible only by virtue of continuous increase in the size of the unit of movement, that is, the individual flotilla of barges, lashed together by cables and propelled by a single power unit, the familiar "towboat" pushing its "tow."

A modern tow in open water, such as the Mississippi River below St. Louis, often carries as much as 40,000 tons of freight instead of the maximum of about 20,000 tons during the early 1950's. Progressive innovation in carrier equipment, associated with improved navigation facilities, has combined with rising sophistication in carrier operations to produce this result.

Unlike the open oceans or the Great Lakes, the central problem of design for large units of movement on the rivers arises from the shallow and circuitous channels, with widely varying seasonal current velocities and water levels. A modern tow of barges may be a quarter

◄ Passing tows on Pickwick Lake, a part of the Tennessee River waterway system.

of a mile long, longer than the 253,000-ton supertanker, *Esso Scotia* (1,148 feet). Any pilot trying to maneuver such a flotilla through the narrow, shifting, and shallow channels of the inland rivers against a swift current, equipped only with the artistry of Mark Twain, would throw up his hands in despair. The answer to this problem has been found in push-towing with very powerful towboats, designed for high maneuverability, and equipped with sophisticated controls.

By reducing the number of separated vessel bows, push-towing cuts down water resistance by about 60 percent. Pull-towing, such as that prevailing on European rivers, congests the channel but doesn't move so much tonnage. With pull-towing on a short hawser, the trailing vessel bobs and founders in the wake of the towboat. When the tow line is lengthened, the towed hull is likely to run aground in tricky currents and on sharp bends in the channel. Slowing, or stopping a pulled tow, especially when moving downstream, is difficult and sometimes impossible. By contrast, a push-tow in pool water can normally be stopped in about 1½ tow lengths by reversing the propellers. It is only by virtue of push-towing that the American rivers move the greatest tonnage of any inland system in the world with congestion only at outmoded locks.

The key to high-tonnage push-towing is the diesel-powered, screw-propelled towboat. The power of towboats has been increasing year by year, from an average (which includes a large number of small harbor craft) of 672 horsepower in 1962 to 1,006 horsepower 10 years later. Towboats having 5,000 or 6,000 horsepower are common, and several of 10,000 horsepower will soon be in service.

Low horsepower requirement is one of the inherent advantages of water transportation. The average horsepower per ton moved on the railroads falls in the range of 0.8 to 2.6, and highway trucking requires about 7.0 horsepower per ton. On the inland rivers, the horsepower requirement per ton generally falls in the range of 0.1 to 0.25. The rising horsepower of towboats thus means a corresponding increase in the tonnage moved with a single crew in a single tow of barges.

To achieve the result of higher power, and, therefore, of higher tonnages of cargo per vessel, the inland shipbuilding industry conducts a continuing research program, utilizing such facilities as the 827-foot tank of the Netherlands Ship Model Basin in Wageningen, Holland, and the U. S. Navy Model Basin in Carderock, Maryland.

Problems are complex—and solutions interdependent. For example, should increased power be delivered by means of larger diameter propellers, additional propellers, increased number of blades, or alteration of blade contours? Whatever decision is made, the structure of the ship will have to be altered accordingly. A typical cost of a 3,200-horsepower towboat is $1,400,000. To get 1,800 additional horsepower, for a total of 5,000, this cost goes up by $200,000. But to get still an additional increment of 1,400 horsepower, for a total of 6,400, the associated increment to cost is $600,000. The reason? The higher horsepower vessels require larger propellers and therefore the hulls must be wider.

The bigger the tow, the greater the premium on maneuverability. The towboat has to push a rigid mass of barges in a narrow and sinuous channel, with or against a current, and around some bends whose radii may be no more than the length of one to two barge tows. Maneuverability is obtained by multiple screws (usually two) which operate independently of each other, each with a steering rudder behind it and two backing, or flanking, rudders before. So equipped, a skillful pilot can pivot a tow of barges, 1,200 feet long, in its own length. He can move his towboat sideways, like a crab, as when extracting a single barge from a full tow.

Controls are highly refined. A sonic depth-finder, far away on the bow of the forward barge, reports its soundings in the pilot house. In darkness, dual searchlights follow the riverbanks, and in both fog and darkness the radar scope sweeps the river for navigation buoys and unexpected obstacles. In the words of one towboat pilot, unlighted objects in a channel have included "a 30-foot luxury cruiser sleeping six, whose owner has had a very relaxed evening and has anchored squarely in the middle of the navigable channel without lights." Radar permits continuous operation in all kinds of weather, day and night, with obvious major economies in labor and overhead.

In the midst of all this engineering, the inland shipbuilder has to construct a floating hotel with air conditioned quarters for a crew of 9 to 14 persons, and often with guest quarters of two or more staterooms with twin beds, private bath, and lounge with TV set and refrigerator. Crew quarters are equipped with recreation area and television. Galley and dining area must be supplemented with food storage space for some 30 days. A laundry room with washer and drier is often included for the convenience of the crew.

This, then, is the product of inland shipbuilding—a floating mass of amenities and sophisticated technology which propels tens of thousands of tons of production and materials of the nation's industry and agriculture.

Barges, while less complex, are far from simple. Unlike oceangoing ships, barges are subjected to intense transverse strains in tow maneuvering, but cannot economically tolerate elaborate reinforcing because of shallow-draft limitations on capacity. They must be highly resistant to impact under the intense pressures of external contact with mooring walls and the like, and also on the interior with clamshell buckets and other unloading devices. Inexpert loading places severe strains on the barge hull more usually than is true of ocean vessels.

Hopper barges, both open and covered, are the pack mules of the waterways. They carry almost anything that isn't liquid—grain, coal, ores, steel, machinery, salt, sugar, sulphur, dry bulk chemicals, sand, fertilizers, and crushed stone. Hopper barges represent the largest share of many waterways operators' barge investment. Cost, therefore, must be low. A typical open hopper barge, 35 feet wide and 195 feet long, with a capacity of 1,450 tons, costs new about $115,000. This is about $79 per ton of capacity. By way of comparison, new open hopper railway cars in the early 1970's cost about $180 per ton of capacity. Hopper barge covers must be designed for light weight, watertight protection, resistance to deflection, and maximum accessibility to the hold when open.

An increasing portion of both hopper barges and tank barges are double-skinned. This reflects the rising values of waterborne cargoes and vulnerability to contamination. A barge often carries a succession of cargoes incompatible with each other, such, for example, as coal northbound on the Mississippi River and grains southbound. The inner skin is unencumbered by structural members, permitting rapid and thorough cleaning. In addition, the inner skin prevents contamination from bilge water. In the event of accident involving puncturing of the hull of a tank barge, the inner skin confines hazardous cargoes, such as certain chemicals or flammable materials, preventing leakage into the river current. Double skinned tank barges are now more popular than single-skinned. Such a barge, 35 feet by 195 feet, costs from $195,000 to $250,000.

Standards of cargo care become ever more exacting. Anhydrous ammonia or chlorine may be carried in barge tanks under pressures of 250 pounds per square inch or more. Temperatures in the range of —260° up to 200° Fahrenheit may be maintained. A growing number of barge tanks have protective linings of such materials as aluminum, stainless steel, plastic, or rubber. By such developments, the variety of cargoes which may be transported by water is increasing continuously.

Unlike the deep-draft shipbuilder, the inland industry must design its product for operation in a strait jacket. Overhead bridge clearances create another waterway dimension in addition to depth and width of channel which must be taken into consideration. Bridge clearances range all the way from those of the adequate height to those in the Chicago area which are so low as to require retractable pilothouses. Lock chambers vary from a width of 66 feet with lengths of 400 feet or 600 feet, to a width of 110 feet with lengths of 600 feet, 800 feet, or 1,200 feet. Standard length barges of 195 feet by 35 feet can be made up three abreast and five long for passage through a 1,200-foot lock. At times two or three barges can be towed alongside at the rear of the towboat. This size tow by double locking can pass through a lock 110 feet wide by 600 feet long.

While total sales of the industry are not publicly reported, they are probably not much in excess of $300 million per year, and may aggregate even less. Units of sale, though, are big. As we have noted previously, individual barges are priced in the range of $115,000 to $250,000 and line-haul towboats from $1,500,000 up—the largest as high as $3,000,000. But, most of the industry's revenue comes from barges. There are more of them. In a typical year, the industry builds 16 to 20 new barges for every towboat constructed.

The increasing tonnage carried in the average tow of barges is matched, of course, by the rising number of towboats in the higher power categories. This development reflects the practice of designing the individual towboat with a view to the characteristics of the waterway in which it is to perform its principal service. Navigation conditions vary enormously as between respective reaches of the waterway system. Water carriers often assign the individual towboat to service in a particular reach, and the vessel is designed for the particular conditions to be encountered there.

The most powerful towboats operate principally on the lower Mississippi River, between St. Louis and the Gulf, moving between 40,000 and 50,000 tons of cargo in a single tow. Reliable channel depths the year around combine with the absence of locks to make this possible. But, other streams are less favorable to tows of this size. On those sections of the Ohio River equipped with new 1,200-foot locks, and with high-lift dams backing up deep pools for as much as 100 miles, 20,000 tons is a typical optimum. On the upper Mississippi River, from St. Louis to the Twin Cities, with 600-foot locks, often no more than 15 to 20 miles apart, as well as on the Illinois, the Missouri, the Warrior, and other streams, smaller tows are advisable.

Confronted by these variations and the necessity for moving a growing portion of the traffic over long hauls through a series of unequal streams, the water carriers and shipbuilders, applying such techniques as simulation analysis, have devised optimum towboat capacities for particular reaches of the system. A particular towboat is often thus designed for its own river and stays there most of the time. Barges are interchanged between power units, and, with growing frequency, between carriers, at key interchange points, such as St. Louis or the mouth of the Ohio, for optimum operation on longhaul cargo movements. The growing volume of waterborne commerce facilitates this practice. More frequent arrivals and departures at an interchange point reduce interchange delays.

Inland shipbuilding is highly competitive. Well over 25 builders produce river barges. Shipyards are widely dispersed. Locations include Pittsburgh, Louisville, St. Louis, Nashville; Paducah, Kentucky; Houston, Beaumont and Orange, Texas; and Gulfport, Mississippi. Yet, the individual yard has very little territorial advantage over its competitors. Unlike carriers in other modes of transportation, the individual water carrier acquiring new vessels does not insist on any particular point of delivery. It costs only about $1.00 per mile to transport a new barge empty, so that a purchase 500 miles up or down the river, adding some $500 to the delivered cost, makes little difference for a vessel billed at $75,000 to $150,000. Thus, every shipyard finds itself in competition with every other shipyard on the river and intracoastal waterway system.

Not only is competition active within the industry, the inland shipbuilding industry is also under competitive pressure, however indirectly, from the competition of its carrier customers with each other and with other modes of transportation. Competitive modes include pipelines, long-distance electric energy transmission (in competition with coal haulage), and multiple-car volume railroad movements. The shipbuilding industry prospers and grows only with growth and prosperity of the water carriers. Competition is met, in part, through creative vessel design, directed toward low carrier operating costs. In addition, prices have to be kept at a low level, particularly in view of the limited capital resources of numerous small water carriers.

The consequence of this competition is keen attention to design and to production economies. In contrast to the deep-draft shipbuilding industry, the inland industry produces a large number of vessels of closely similar design, introducing an element of mass production. Component structures, such as pilot houses and bow sections, are prefabricated and transported to assembly sites. Yards are laid out for an efficient flow of materials and subassemblies, incorporating assembly line technique. Each barge weighs in the range of 280 to 545 tons. In spite of this huge weight, in a typical yard, the barge is moved on rails down a four-station assembly line. At the final, or launching, position, the vessel receives not only the finishing and painting, but also a thorough examination and final testing. Capacity output in a big yard runs as high as a barge per day.

The competitive strength of the inland shipbuilding industry is indicated by its ability to construct occasional seagoing vessels, delivered down the rivers to the coasts. Occasionally ships built inland are exported, usually for inland waterway service abroad. Whether or not the U. S. inland shipyards can match foreign construction costs is a moot question. Their real superiority is that of design. It is difficult for even the most ingenious ship designers abroad to match American skill in shallow-draft vessel design. Lacking an inland river and carrier system comparable to that of the United States, the momentum of innovation remains less developed. In addition, U. S. inland shipbuilding offers superior design in channel maintenance vessels, drilling vessels, and the like. Products of the U. S. inland shipbuilding industry are serving on the Seine in France, the Adriatic Sea and the rivers of Africa.

The production line techniques of inland shipbuilders carry a special bonus for their carrier customers, prompt delivery of barges. Towboats take longer —some eight to nine months—the yards could build them more quickly than this, but such components as engines and propeller forgings and shafts are acquired from outside suppliers, and these take several months. A barge can take anywhere from three weeks to ten weeks to build, depending upon complexity and assuming that steel can be delivered promptly by the supplier.

Inland shipbuilding is a reserve national defense facility in the same sense as deep-draft shipbuilding on the coasts. Federal policy recognizes and partially finances the U. S. deep-draft shipbuilding industry in this role. This is reflected in construction differential subsidies for ships engaged in foreign trade. Subsidies are pointed toward capability in the production of naval or military auxiliary vessels. While the inland shipbuilding industry possesses this capability, it is not eligible for such subsidies, of course, because its products are utilized only in domestic commerce. Capability for producing naval and military auxiliary vessels was well proven in World War II by the inland construction of large numbers of such vessels. One of the shipyards on the Ohio River turned out 149 ships of various types for the armed forces, ships which played a role in the North African, Pacific and European campaigns. On the Illinois Waterway, 1,200 war vessels including 28 submarines and 72 oceangoing military cargo vessels were constructed. Some of these moved to sea via the Great Lakes. A large number, however, were moved down the Mississippi River to the Gulf of Mexico.

In a national emergency, the inland river vessels conserve scarce materials and components. During World War II, such components as castings, forgings, and machined parts were in acutely short supply. Requiring only one power unit for the movement of 10,000 tons or more of freight, the inland vessel drew less upon such components than other modes. Inland ships likewise conserve such scarce materials as steel. For example, a 306-ton steel barge carries 10,900 barrels of gasoline, that is, 35.7 barrels per ton of steel. By contrast, a railway car of 24 tons of steel carries about 240 barrels, or 10 barrels per ton of steel. During World War II, submarine attacks on coastwise tankers diverted the movement of petroleum products from the high seas to inland routings. River barging took over much of the task with a minimum drain on scarce components and materials.

As for the future of inland shipbuilding, the challenge of creative innovation remains as great as ever. New vessel concepts are under development. One is that of deep-draft barges and push towboats for the open oceans and the Great Lakes. A tow of river barges, tailored as it is to river requirements, is not seaworthy on the oceans and lakes. However, single-barge push-towing on the Gulf of Mexico and along the coasts is already under way. Push-towing eliminates the hawser of pull-towing, with its attendant drag, and reduces the water resistance of a second vessel bow. The barge is constructed with a notch in the stern for the bow of the tug. Officials of one company report that in operations between Florida and Louisiana over the Gulf of Mexico they can utilize push-towing 85 percent of the time. In heavy seas, the tug reverts to pull-towing.

The individual barge so propelled has a capacity up to 26,000 tons, comparable to the largest carriers on the Great Lakes. The system permits drastic reduction in crew size as opposed to a conventional ship and liberates the power unit and crew for productive activity while the barge is being loaded and unloaded. Commodities now being moved by this system include coal, fertilizer materials, and sugar. The future expansion of this system offers high promise.

Containerization is another field of promise. Oceangoing ships for the transport of van-sized containers are especially designed and outfitted for this service, including an elaborate structural system within the hold for receiving and securing the containers. As the volume of container movement grows, carriage in river barges, especially between the upper Mississippi Valley and the Gulf Coast, appears in prospect. This development may well call for special design and construction of container barges similar in principle to existing container ships.

Changes in the dimensions of the navigation system hold out new challenges and opportunities to inland shipbuilding. We have already noted vessel and tow design adaptation to the new 1,200-foot locks on a portion of the Ohio River. During the coming years, the necessity for constructing dual lockage installations of approximately this dimension on the remainder of the Ohio and on the Illinois River will very probably induce such construction. Continued improvements on the upper Mississippi River and other major streams will play a role.

A major overhaul in vessel design concepts will attend the eventual establishment of a 12-foot channel, in place of the present limiting depth of 9 feet, over much of the Mississippi River System. Such a development will make a major contribution to both economy and safety of river navigation, a contribution from which both commercial and recreational boating will benefit. It will certainly call for drastic redesign of vessels. Barges will be designed not only for greater depth, but, because of the increased strength imparted by depth, of greater length. River barges of 5,000 tons capacity are a realistic possibility. Towboats of greater draft can be designed for greater power. Tows of barges carrying as much as 75,000 tons each are conceivable, but, in spite of their greater tonnage, occupying no more channel space and safer in operation than their present counterparts of much lesser tonnage.

The Coming Role of Barging In Marine Container Operations

The Seabee and the LASH (lighter-aboard-ship) systems are ships that take loaded river barges aboard and transport them on the high seas as cargo carriers. Lifted off the ships in Europe and the United States, these same barges move far inland on the navigable rivers to discharge and pick up cargo. In this way, ocean shipping and shallow-draft inland transportation are wedded.

Many of the barge-carrying ships also transport loaded van containers, that is, truck vans without their running gear. Numerous other ships in overseas commerce carry van containers only. Discharged from the ships, the loaded vans are put back on their wheels or placed on railway flat cars for movement inland.

Thus, the van container has been conceived as interchangeable among all modes of surface transportation except barging. One marine executive refers to van containerization as "an integrated truck-rail-ship through service system." Shouldn't he also have mentioned barging?

The executive's oversight is understandable. Containerized movements are supposed to be fast; barging slow. Van containers carry high-valued general cargo; barges mostly bulk. Van containers carry small lots. A 20-ton van load is a big one. Barging calls for big lots. A 300-ton barge shipment is a small one. It would appear that van containerization and barging are incompatible.

But, this is mostly a matter of image. There is, in fact, every reason to expect that barging will play a large role in the intermodal movement of van containers. And, the barge-carrying ships promise to be an important spur to the achievement of this role.

The barging of van containers will probably develop mostly in conjunction with ocean shipping—principally foreign trade. Marine carriage is the big growth segment of containerization. In domestic commerce, the demountable van container has been promoted with some vigor by a few railroads. But, in competition with conventional piggyback trailer movement, containerization in domestic commerce has not grown proportionately. In 1964, van containers carried in the U. S. by all modes were 10 percent of total piggyback. In 1971, they were down to 4 percent.

Then, who is buying all the van containers? Over 116,000 were built during the 10 years preceding 1972. They are going principally into marine carriage. The Port of New York Authority reports that containerization saves an average of $12 a ton in export packaging and at least $8 a ton in overseas transportation. To attain these, or greater savings, most general cargo is now moving in containers. One maritime authority says, "Nearly 80% of the general cargo moving across the Atlantic can be placed in containers." Economists project close to 450,000 U. S.-built van containers in maritime service by 1980. The containers are going to sea.

So it is that the container is pictured as a ship-truck and a ship-rail facility. But, it's just as logical that river barges should become important carriers of van containers to and from the seaports. The navigable rivers all connect the seaports with inland centers. Let's look at the pattern which the movement of marine containers is already assuming. It is a pattern into which the barge fits neatly.

Marine container movements are developing around the feeder-ship. The big trans-Atlantic container vessels represent an enormous investment. Their container holds are highly specialized and ill-adapted to other cargo. The box-shaped container does not utilize well the internal space of the ship's hold with its curved conformation. Thus, to move the yearly tonnage necessary to justify the investment, it is essential to keep these trans-Atlantic container ships under way at sea as much as possible. Therefore, the feeder-ship—and the barge.

Under the feeder-ship concept, the trans-oceanic container vessels operate as shuttle carriers, stopping normally at only two major ports on each side of the ocean, thereby minimizing time in port and in coastwise movement. On the Gulf Coast, New Orleans and Houston promise to be such ports. Most containerized cargo for an entire coastal reach is thus to be loaded and unloaded only at these major ports. From the major ports, feeder-ships fan out to serve off-shore points and coastal ports of lesser tonnage, such as Mobile, Lake Charles and Baton Rouge. But, if feeder-ships are to operate between New Orleans and such other ports, why not feeder-barges as well? Barges can provide an equivalent service in the sheltered waters of the intracoastal waterways and the Mississippi River, for example.

Furthermore, if barges are to provide a feeder service between such ports as New Orleans and Baton Rouge, why not also between New Orleans and St. Louis, or Cincinnati, or Chicago? The feeder-barge and the feeder-ship are the same thing in principle—excepting that the barge is more flexible, operating in shallow-draft as well as deep-draft waters.

This conception resolves the problem of lot size—of the 20-ton van versus the 1,500-ton barge. The decisive appeal of the van container is its linkage of small-lot movements to big-tonnage vessels. The drive behind containerization is the speed with which it permits the transfer of small-lot general cargo between ship and shore—or between ship and ship.

A conventional general cargo ship spends most of its time in port, and 60 to 75 percent of the cost of transporting general cargo by sea is accounted for by what takes place while the ship is at the dock and not by steaming time. The cost of holding a ship in port commonly falls in the range of $4,000 to $4,500 a day. The complete unloading and reloading time of a general cargo ship by old-fashioned, conventional methods normally ranges from five to eight days. But, with a container ship, the same operation takes less than a single 24-hour day, and with fewer men. Because of this, three container ships can carry an annual tonnage of five conventional ships, and cargo handling costs are reduced in the range of 65 to 80 percent. The essence of the van container is thus its establishment of low-cost compatibility between the small-lot shipment and the 12,000-ton ocean vessel.

Now if the van container establishes compatibility of the 20-ton van with the 12,000-ton ship, why not also with the 1,500-ton barge in the same port? And, if it permits expeditious and safe transfer between the transoceanic shuttle-ship and the feeder-ship, why not also between shuttle-ship and barge? The deep-draft ships, of course, have a built-in internal supporting structure for container stowage. Barges can be constructed this way, too. But, a large portion of marine container movement is deck cargo. In the case of refrigerated cargo, it has to be on the deck for servicing. Likewise, conventional barges can handle containers as deck cargo.

In fact, in important respects, the barge as a container carrier is superior to the deep-draft ship. Container shipping on the open ocean has to contend with the immense internal stresses of irregularly stowed cargo moving in heavy seas. Most barges move only in sheltered waters. Containers carried as deck cargo on barges raise fewer difficulties of load distribution and of instability.

The element of time in transit, of course, raises an additional question. Marine container service is much faster than conventional handling. Officials of United States Lines announce that by combining rail-truck carriage with marine container handling, they can often move cargo between Chicago and Basel, Switzerland, for example, in 12 to 14 days. This is a saving of some 10 to 12 days as compared with conventional handling—a typical time reduction. Barges are relatively slow, but lower in cost. Does this argue against the compatibility between the van container and the barge? On the contrary, it argues as well in favor of that compatibility.

The barge is an alternative to overland rail and truck carriage between internal points and the seaport. The barge takes more time. From St. Louis downbound with the current to New Orleans, a barge will take a day or two longer than rail or truck; upbound against the current, it may take three or four days longer. But the differential is less with respect to points closer to the coast. From Memphis, Tennessee, barge movement represents only an extra day in either direction. On an overall schedule of 12 to 14 days for the entire movement, the extra time is a relatively small addition—about the equivalent of what bad weather at sea is likely to do in any case. The barge, as opposed to rail or truck, adds only moderately to overall time, and affects even less the precision of scheduling.

Let's note again that the decisive appeal of marine containerization is cost saving—not time saving. The time saving is a by-product. For some shippers, time saving is very important, and they will not want to sacrifice any of it. But, for larger numbers, attracted to containerization by its governing appeal of reduced cost, the still further cost reduction of barge movement between the inland point and the seaport will add to the container's attractiveness.

We have noted that on a typical inland-to-inland overseas movement, conventional cargo handling requires some 24 days, and that rail-truck-ship container movement will cut this to about 14 days. Suppose, then, that container barge handling, as an alternative to rail and truck, adds some three days to the reduced 14-day time. The shipper still enjoys a reduction in total time from 24 to 17 days—something like a week. For many shippers, this is more than good enough.

If all this is true, why aren't more containers moving in barges? The answer is that marine containerization is still in its developmental stages. Containerized handling cannot operate effectively in conventionally equipped port areas, but requires specialized, high-volume marine container terminals. For this reason, containerization has made its first big breakthrough in the Port of New York area and, to a lesser degree, in the Bay area of the Pacific Coast.

On the Gulf Coast, marine containerization at the ports of Houston and New Orleans is in its earlier stages. The Gulf Coast, of course, with its inland connections via the Mississippi River System is that to which containerized barging will make its fullest contribution. Gulf Coast potentials are very high, representing something well over 25 percent of all container-adapted outbound U. S. liner cargo.

There is little doubt that marine containerization will grow. Indeed, it appears likely that within something like the next 10 to 15 years, most general cargo to and from overseas points will move either by marine containers or air transport, leaving only a residue for conventional handling.

Marine containerization is a response to rising port costs—mostly to rising wage rates for longshore and maritime labor. There is probably no large segment of the transportation system more primitive in its methods or more wasteful of labor than conventional ship-shore handling of general cargo. The average productivity of New York longshoremen has been measured at 0.45 long tons (1,008 lbs.) of general cargo per manhour. With constantly rising wage rates, in the era of such labor-saving developments as the articulated barge tow of 40,000 tons and the unit train, the conventional dock procedures became progressively more anachronistic and intolerable. If the wage levels of the early 1960's were high enough to inspire the beginnings of marine containerization, those of the late 1970's will make it sweep the waterfront.

Much, or most, of the general cargo moving through the Gulf Coast will, in the course of time, almost certainly go into containers. Extensive marshalling areas have been staked out for container storage and handling. For an extended period, Sea-Land Service, Inc., has been offering weekly container service via Houston, and in October 1968, Lykes Bros. Steamship Co. initiated container service via New Orleans for the Military Sea Transportation Service, announcing its intention to seek commercial container cargoes in conjunction with this operation. The Gulf Coast breakthrough is now taking place, and with it will come direct access to the most extensive inland waterway system in the country, reaching to such cities as Memphis, St. Louis, Cincinnati, and Chicago.

The present developmental stage of containerization limits container barging also because of the shortage of marine container equipment. Cargoes are expedited via rail and truck for maximum utilization of containers and container ships, accounting for the present emphasis on speed. But, this will change. As we have seen, containers are being manufactured in large quantity. Container ships on the ways offer capacities so large as to generate anxiety among marine carriers as to future excess capacity. As more equipment becomes available, the urgency of speed will decline, and the element of the cost of transportation will resume its normal priority.

We have noted that, because a number of Seabee and LASH ships are equipped to carry containers as well as barges, these vessels constitute the portal through which barging may be expected to make its large-scale entry into marine van container service. Barging shares one other advantage with these ships—the conservation of scarce deep-draft wharfage space on the waterfront.

Unlike conventional general cargo vessels, LASH and Seabee ships can take aboard and discharge their barges in open harbor waters away from the piers. The barges themselves, of course, are loaded and unloaded at shallow-draft terminals. The system thus makes no necessary demand on scarce and high-priced deep-draft wharfage space.

Likewise, container-carrying barges can be loaded and unloaded at terminals along the many miles of readily available shallow-draft frontage. Barge-borne van containers, in turn, can be transferred to and from containerships in open harbor waters. Van container staging areas served by railroads and trucks make enormous demands on scarce deep-draft waterfront land. Container barging, by contrast, can be based on the more abundant shallow-draft frontage.

Thus, van containers and river barges represent a high degree of compatability, and in the movement and handling of containers, the barge offers genuine advantages over land modes. The container barge holds a position of high promise in American shipping.

Waterway User Charges and Foreign Competition

It has frequently been pointed out that user charges on U. S. waterways would impair the position of American industry as against foreign competition. Waterway user charges would reduce exports, encourage imports, and put adverse pressure on the U. S. balance of payments.

Some very capable economists remain skeptical. For example, one commented that the above argument would seem to call for user charges on upstream movement of imported goods but not on downstream movements for export. His economic logic is superficially plausible. But, his premises are false.

Let's take a careful look at some of the realities of domestic water transportation and foreign competition.

All official proposals for the imposition of user charges on the U. S. inland waterways contemplate the total exemption of foreign commerce moving in American waters. Such exemption appears unavoidable.

Numerous treaty obligations, the sensitivity of diplomatic relations, and the variety of economic weapons in the foreign arsenal of retaliation argue conclusively against user charges on foreign commerce. It may be taken as a fixed position of the user charge movement that foreign commerce would be exempt.

Foreign commerce moves on the U.S. rivers and canals in the same traffic stream and in direct competition with both deep-draft and shallow-draft domestic carriage. Of the total ton-miles of freight carried on all the rivers and canals of this country, over 15 percent consists of foreign commerce, a high percentage of which moves in foreign flag ships. On a tonnage basis, the percentage would be higher.

Where is this foreign commerce going? It is moving between the open seas and the inland seaports. Baton Rouge, for example, is 233 miles inland, Houston 52 miles, and Albany, N. Y., 144 miles. Of the total river and canal system of the country, 2,324 miles consist of deep-draft, sheltered waters such as these—some of the most heavily traveled inland waters in the country.

In recent years, foreign commerce has been penetrating ever farther inland. Oceangoing ships have come all the way up the Mississippi River to St. Louis, Missouri, and a few as far as Louisville, Kentucky, on the Ohio River.

In 1971, 1.6 million tons of European and Asian steel were unloaded at Houston, Texas. To get there, the foreign steel had to move in from the Gulf northbound up the 52-mile ship channel.

In that same year, 787,000 tons of domestic steel moved northbound in that same ship channel in shallow-draft barges to Houston. It had come by river and the Gulf Intracoastal Waterway all the way from inland origins, such as

▲ Deckhand securing safety line between two barges in a tow.

Pittsburgh and Chicago. An additional 195,000 tons of domestic steel reach Houston in coastwise ships, for a total of 982,000 tons of waterborne American steel moving, with the foreign steel, in the same northbound stream of traffic to the same port. Now, how can anybody justify slapping a charge for northbound use of the Houston Ship Channel on the domestic steel and letting the foreign steel go free?

Houston is only part of the picture. In 1971, nearly 4.0 million tons of finished steel from overseas were moved up the rivers and channels to Gulf Coast ports—into the Sabine-Neches Waterway, up the Mississippi River to New Orleans and Baton Rouge, into Mobile Bay, and other coastal waters. That same year, 1.5 million tons of domestic steel moved by shallow-draft barges into those same markets, most of it all the way from Pittsburgh.

The damage of waterway user charges to the American steel industry would be considerable. The f.o.b. value of domestic steel shipped by barge to Gulf Coast markets exceeds $300 million per year. Any of the user charge proposals, at high cost-recovery standards, of the last 10 years would have raised the cost of steel barging by over 20 percent, and some as much as 50 percent. The barging distance from Pittsburgh to the Gulf is about 2,000 miles, and a user charge on a mileage basis, such as a fuel tax, could easily give the coup de grace to this movement, surrendering the Gulf Coast steel market to the Japanese and the Common Market.

Iron ore imports have risen from 8 percent of total U. S. receipts in 1950 to 35 percent in 1971. Most of these imports enter the country via U. S. waters up the Delaware River and Chesapeake Bay. The biggest portion of domestic ore moves by lake out of the Lake Superior district to Lake Erie destinations. At Lake Erie, ore is transshipped into the Youngstown and Pittsburgh steel-making districts.

In the Youngstown and Pittsburgh districts, the U. S. ore collides head-on with the foreign iron ore brought into these same districts from the Delaware River. There is certainly no economic logic which could justify loading a use tax on domestic lake ore for Pittsburgh-Youngstown consumption and leaving the directly competitive foreign ore free from such a tax in the government-maintained channels of the Atlantic Coast.

The Minnesota and Michigan iron ore industry is not the only domestic interest at stake. Let's remember that domestic Great Lakes ore is carried exclusively in U. S. vessels. A good portion of the foreign ore, however, comes into the country in foreign flag ships. Thus, any use tax or charge exclusively on the domestic movements would be a flagrant discrimination against U. S. shipping.

In 1971, over 594 million bushels of corn, wheat, oats, barley, rye, and soybeans were shipped down the Illinois, the Missouri, and the Mississippi Rivers to Baton Rouge, New Orleans, and other Gulf Coast ports. These waterborne products generated a farm income exceeding $1 billion that year, principally on farms in the basin states of the Missouri, the Illinois, and the Upper Mississippi Rivers.

Most of these waterborne farm products were exported. The Board of Commissioners of the Port of New Orleans states that between 65 percent and 90 percent of all grain exported from that port arrives from inland by river barge.

Likewise, the Columbia and Snake Rivers in the Pacific Northwest originate large quantities of export grain. In 1971, 51 million bushels of grain were barged down the Snake and Columbia Rivers, principally for export. Grain exports delivered to the coast by river barge are an important sector of American farm income.

The impact of user charges on the waterborne carriage of farm crops would be very severe. As an example, federal cost-recovery user charges officially proposed in 1972 would have raised the cost of transporting corn from central Illinois to Gulf Coast ports from about 10 cents to 18.5 cents a bushel. An increase of this magnitude would have eliminated the movement.

As Carl J. Lessing, former vice president of the Chicago Board of Trade, recently said: "We would be hard pressed to name a commodity whose pricing is more sensitive to transportation charges than grain, as grain is marketed in large volumes with low unit costs. It is not uncommon to lose sales for differences of one-quarter of a cent per bushel. . . ."

The grain movement illustrates well the user charge distortion of port relationships. Export grain barged down the Mississippi River may be transshipped to ocean vessels at either Baton Rouge or New Orleans, 133 miles farther downstream. If the grain were transshipped at Baton Rouge, from there to New Orleans and beyond it would be in foreign trade and exempt from the user charge. But, if the grain were to continue in domestic barging beyond Baton Rouge to the public elevator at New Orleans, for the 133-mile distance between the two cities, it would remain in domestic commerce and subject to the user charge.

Thus, we would have the astonishing spectacle of export grain moving in the same southbound direction in the same stream of traffic between these two ports, that still in domestic commerce subject to the user charge, that transshipped to foreign commerce exempt. The bias in favor of the upstream port is obvious. The same discrimination would be inflicted as between Houston and Galveston, New York and Albany, San Francisco and Sacramento, and other port systems, a discrimination totally lacking in any economic justification.

The three movements we have cited—steel, iron ore, and grains—are big income producers in the domestic economy. We could add others, notably chemicals, crude oil, gasoline, newsprint, and other high-value products. When we cite 1.5 million tons of domestic waterborne steel carried by barge to the Gulf Coast and 594 million bushels of grain barged down the Mississippi, obviously the dollar involvement runs in the hundreds of millions. Add to this the loss of shipping by U. S. flag vessels in coastwise movement and on the Great Lakes, and the adverse impact on the balance of payments begins to look impressive.

The major domestic waterborne commodity movements have assumed a pattern highly strengthening to U. S. production as against foreign competition, and a user charge would destroy much of that advantage. Any valid evaluation of the user charge impact must be premised on these facts.

The Coming Transportation Crunch and the Potentials Of Barging Technology

New technologies in water transportation will make an important contribution towards averting a transportation crunch in the late 1970's and the 1980's. The transportation needs of a rapidly expanding economy are unrelenting. Unless our intercity freight haulage system modernizes and expands in full pace with rising production, the country's industries and commerce can become snarled in tie-ups and delays, with an inflationary impact on costs.

The Transportation Association of America reports that from 1961 to 1971 the GNP, stated in dollars of constant purchasing power, rose by 48 percent. During the same ten years, ton-miles of freight hauled intercity throughout the United States increased at virtually the same rate. By 1985, we may expect GNP to jump by another 85 to 90 percent. The demand for freight transportation will make the same leap.

All modes are feeling the pressure. While traffic on the waterways and highways continued to mushroom from 1961 to 1971, ton-miles hauled on the railroads expanded over one-third faster than on the highways and over twice as much as on the waterways. Referring to the growth outlook, John P. Fishwick, President of the Norfolk & Western Railway commented: "The question is: How can the railroads handle this enormous additional business?" The answer, of course, is the same for both the waterways and the railroads, as well as for other modes. An expansion in capacity must be achieved on a scale without precedent in a short time.

The demands upon investment, both public and private, will be enormous. Fortunately, however, in expanding the capacity of water carriage, the investment, particularly the public sector, is greatly conserved by new water carriage technologies. Private enterprise, utilizing these technologies, stands ready to wring a maximum volume of freight service out of new improvements in the waterway system.

Water carriage produces more ton-miles of freight movement per mile of right-of-way than any other surface mode. In 1971, on the 25,543 miles of rivers and canals in the United States, the water carriers moved, on the average, over 8.0 million ton-miles per mile. The corresponding figure for the railroads was 3.6 million, less than half as much.

This achievement was the product of past waterway improvements and the new technologies these improvements induced. In their unimproved state, the inland rivers and coastal channels alternated between destructive floods and impassably low water. Operating costs were high. Service was not only seasonal, but subject to unpredictable interruptions, sometimes of long duration. Under these conditions, there was little incentive for the water carriers to develop operating efficiencies. Operating standards and vessel design remained close to those of the old western river steamboats of the late 1800's.

The new era of improved waterway standards was ushered in by the completion in 1929 of the original canalization of the Ohio River. This project established a minimum channel depth of 9 feet the year around. From that time on, river transportation between the industrial center of Pittsburgh and the expanding markets of the South and Southwest became a 365-day-a-year operation. Other river developments soon followed. The Illinois River improvements opened the route from Chicago to the same markets in 1935. Canalization of the Upper Mississippi from St. Louis to St. Paul and Minneapolis was completed in the late 1930's. Other programs included canalization of the Tennessee River and recanalization of the Warrior-Tombigbee, as well as channel development on the Missouri River and the Gulf Intracoastal Waterway.

The national program of multi-purpose water resource development of the Congress had many objectives, of course, including flood control, land erosion abatement, bank stabilization, electric power potential and recreation. But, the development of the rivers as a transportation resource was a major objective, interrelated with the others, and heightened by the urgent needs of agriculture and of economically depressed regions. With the completion of these programs, modern river transportation began its development as a scientific operation.

The new water carriage technologies, introduced during the 1930's and proceeding with acceleration thereafter, exerted a highly expansive influence on the capacity of the navigation system. In evaluating each of the major waterway improvement programs prior to construction, the Corps of Engineers typically underestimated the traffic outlook. In part, this was due to professional conservatism; but, in part, also it reflected the traffic-expanding impact of carrier technologies induced by the improvements themselves and not foreseeable at the time of the forecasts.

The most important technologies have been those contributing to the power and maneuverability of the towboat. These include the substitution of screw propulsion for the paddle-wheel and of the diesel motor for the steam engine, as well as the introduction of the Kort Nozzle. Screw propulsion, with its accompanying rudder system, adds greatly to maneuverability. By judicious combinations of independent screw operation and rudder adjustment, the pilot of a modern towboat can literally make the vessel move sideways. The diesel motor drastically reduces down time and expense for maintenance, while adding greatly to power potential. The Kort Nozzle, a cylindrical housing concentrating the flow of water against the propeller blades, adds some 25 percent to the effective push or thrust of the towboat while under way.

A major consequence of these technologies has been more tonnage per tow. The stern-wheel steamboat typically packed only some 500 or 600 horsepower. Today, 4,800 to 6,000 horsepower is common, and several towboats of 10,000 horsepower will soon be in service. The bigger the tow, of course, the more difficult it is to nurse it through the circuitous channels of the rivers. The highly maneuverable modern towboat counteracts this handicap. A single tow of barges on the Ohio River carried 36,000 tons of Western Kentucky coal. This is a bigger unit of movement than that of most lake carriers.

Of course, bigger tows cut costs per ton, notably those of labor and fuel. But, more to the present point, they also increase the capacity of the navigation system. With greater maneuverability and the more powerful braking action provided by reversing the propellers, the necessary clearances between tows can be reduced without sacrifice of safety. For any given tonnage of movement, fewer tows are in the channel, reducing collision exposure. Locks are often better utilized. A lock may be preempted for just as long a time by a small tow, carrying little tonnage, as by a large one, the latter more fully utilizing the capacity of the chamber.

The installation of radar also raised the yearly capacity of the river channels. Previously, traffic on an otherwise busy stream was completely tied up in foggy weather and other periods of low visibility. By permitting continuous movement, radar controls have expanded the yearly tonnage without a corresponding increase in congestion. The radiotelephone likewise reduces waiting time, especially in meeting oncoming tows in narrow channels and in establishing better communication with shore-based lock crews for expeditious approach. These controls have sharpened the eyes and ears of the pilot, kept the traffic moving, and greatly increased the annual tonnage the channels can carry.

One of the most vital contributors to channel and lockage capacity is a good backhaul balance. One-way movements not only add to costs, they congest the navigation system with empty barges. A string of empty barges ties up a lock just as long as a fully loaded tow, and adds nothing to tonnage.

The canalization of a river is a strong force for developing backhauls. Prior to canalization of such rivers as the Illinois and the Ohio, traffic in the swift currents moved mostly downstream. A canalization system consists of a series of dams, each impounding a long, deep "pool" of slack water. In the new navigation system of the Arkansas River, for example, the river current at Fort Smith has a velocity of less than 3 miles an hour for 75 percent of the time and will rarely exceed 5 miles an hour. On such slack water rivers as the Ohio, the Illinois, and the Upper Mississippi, a good traffic balance has developed. The tonnages moving upstream are now at least equal to those moving down. For example, barges move grain in one direction and coal, fertilizer, and salt in the other. Barges which would otherwise move empty now carry full loads, in many reaches of the rivers actually doubling the annual tonnage of carrying capacity.

In the encouragement of backhaul movements, the ship-to-shore direct company radio communication telephone should also be mentioned. The telephone permits continuous communication between the towboat pilot and shore-based dispatching officers. The improvement of service and of vessel utilization by backhaul carriage is an obvious consequence.

Waterway improvements not only provide capacity of otherwise nonnavigable streams, they also open to traffic channels which already exist. Prior to the canalization of a stream, for example, the channel in fact is actually available to navigation for much of the year, that is, during the high water season. But, little traffic develops because of its seasonal and unpredictable character. In the Nineteenth Century, steamboats penetrated seasonally as far upstream as Fort Smith, Arkansas, and Yankton, South Dakota. This pattern of irregular service has virtually disappeared. A modern electric power plant, chemical plant, or steel mill cannot operate on such a transportation base. The introduction of year-around service generates traffic, not only during the low-water season which the canalization system eliminates, but in the high-water season as well. In other words, the building of navigation capacity for, say, four months of the year generates twelve months of traffic.

Again, the navigation system on a tributary river generates traffic on the main stream, navigable in its natural state. Steel moves from Pittsburgh to Houston, a movement made feasible only by improvement of the Ohio River and the Gulf Intracoastal Waterway. Grain moves from St. Paul to New Orleans, utilizing the canalization system of the Upper Mississippi. But, both of these illustrative movements traverse the Lower Mississippi between St. Louis and the coast, navigable in its natural state. Thus, the ton-miles of traffic generated on a canalized tributary are only a fragment of the ton-miles the improvement generates on the river system as a whole.

Because of new technologies, as well as the inherent character of water transportation, waterway improvements thus exert a multiplier impact on transportation capacity. Before the construction of the St. Lawrence Seaway, certain highly competent, but skeptical, engineers calculated its capacity very carefully at 35 million tons per year. In 1972, the Seaway carried about 50 million tons and was nowhere near its capacity. What happened? Improved technology, a better backhaul pattern, and larger vessel units had raised the ceiling. This is true of most waterway improvements.

Technological improvements continue. The bowthruster, a powered propeller at the forward end of the tow, permits an ever-longer fleet of barges to negotiate sharp bends in the rivers by pivoting on its own radius. Electronic devices and other controls are progressing in depth finders, swing indicators, and engine room automation. Tows of 30 and 40 barges now move with ease. Tows of 50 and 60 barges will eventually bring new and ever greater economies to the commerce of the nation.

The pressure on the nation's transportation system, admittedly, is severe, and the crunch is mounting. Expansion of capacity by all modes must proceed without avoidable delay. But, on the waterways, the potentials of this expansion are promising in the highest degree. Both in the nature of waterway improvement and in the carrier technologies improvements generate, public investment achieves a multiple enlargement of capability in moving the nation's freight. On the U. S. waterways, the expansion of freight-carrying capacity in full measure with the demand of a mounting Gross National Product will be achieved with the highest degree of efficiency in utilization of the public and private investment.

◄ Deckhands ready connecting hose for pumping cargo ashore.

23

the inland waterways of the United States

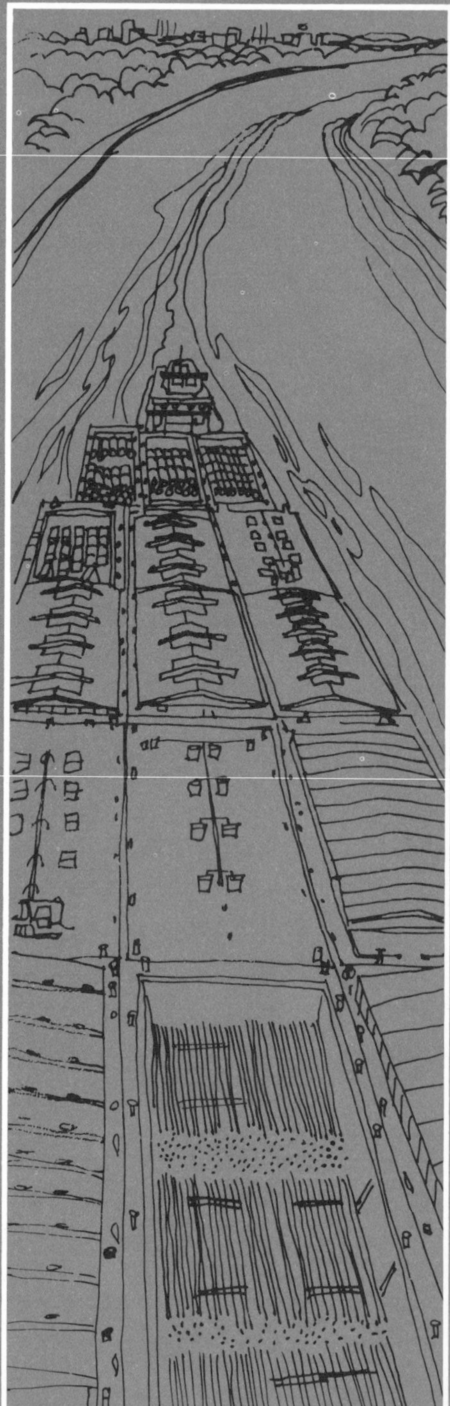

The nation's internal, commercial water routes, except the Great Lakes, are shown in a series of maps which follow.

We have outlined all of the improved and proposed river, canal, and intracoastal channels throughout the United States in a large map inserted in the rear of this book.

Maps of the 27 principal waterways are presented showing total mileages, depths, lock dimensions, principal commodities transported, and major types of industries located along the waterways.

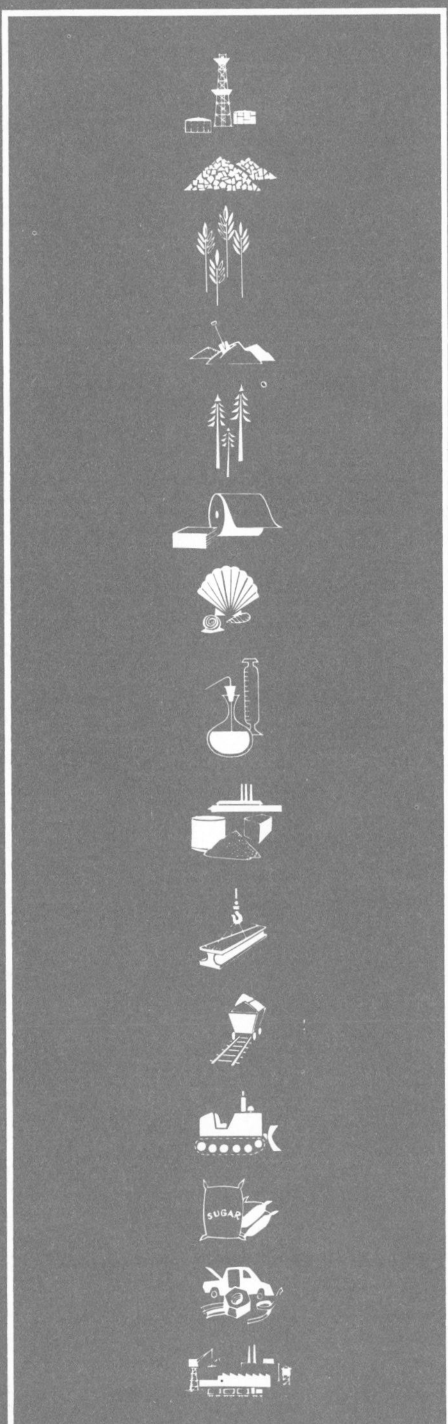

legend

Petroleum and petroleum products

Anthracite coal, bituminous coal and lignite

Grain and grain products

Limestone, sand, gravel and crushed rock, cement

Logs, lumber and lumber products, pulpwood, woodpulp

Paper and paper products

Seashells, unmanufactured

Industrial chemicals

Nonmetallic minerals and manufacturers

Iron and steel products

Ores

Construction, mining machinery and parts

Sugar

Iron and steel scrap

Industrial complex

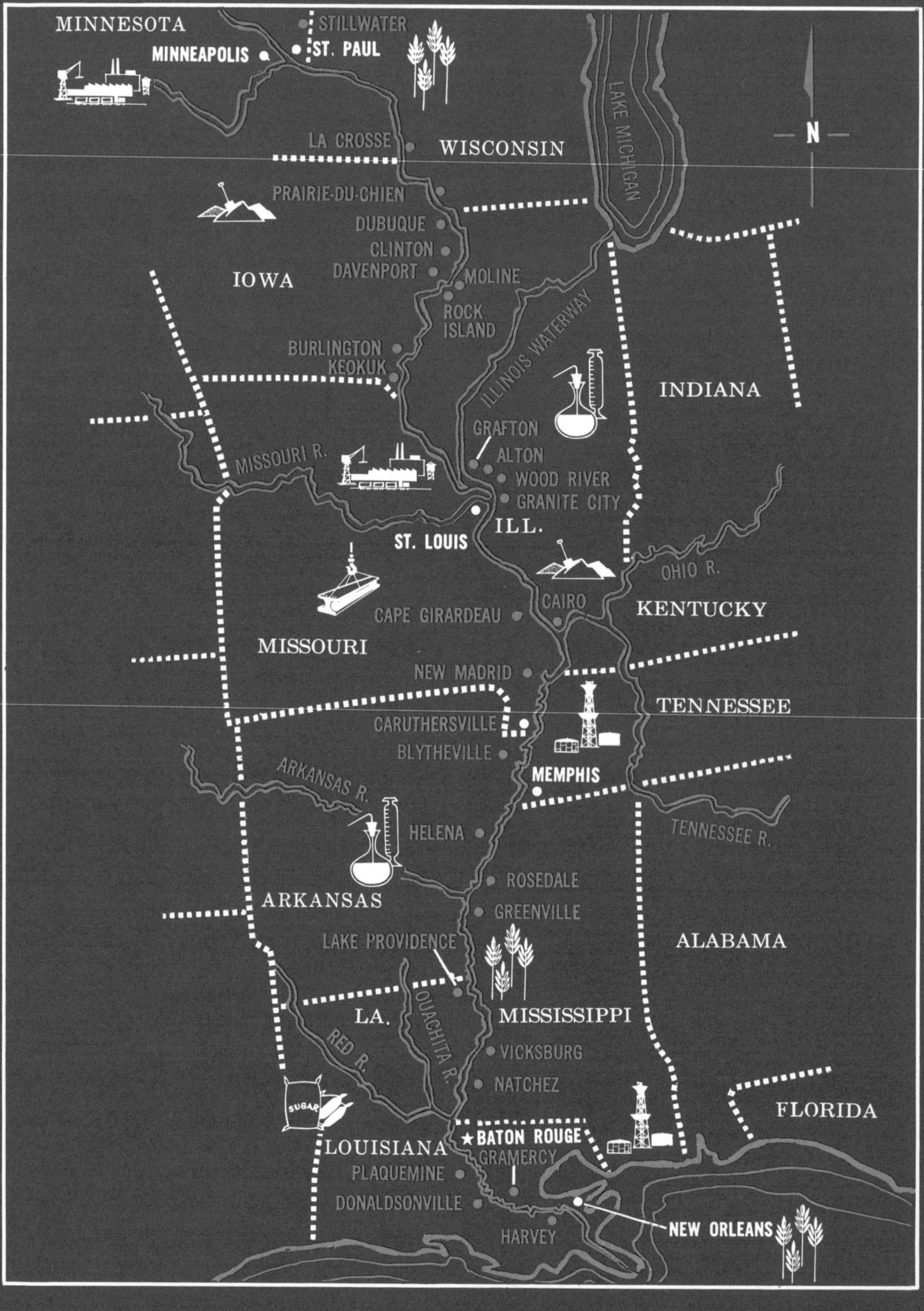
MINNESOTA
MINNEAPOLIS
ST. PAUL
STILLWATER
N
LAKE MICHIGAN
LA CROSSE
WISCONSIN
PRAIRIE-DU-CHIEN
DUBUQUE
CLINTON
DAVENPORT
MOLINE
ROCK ISLAND
IOWA
BURLINGTON
KEOKUK
ILLINOIS WATERWAY
INDIANA
GRAFTON
ALTON
WOOD RIVER
GRANITE CITY
MISSOURI R.
ST. LOUIS
ILL.
OHIO R.
CAIRO
KENTUCKY
CAPE GIRARDEAU
MISSOURI
NEW MADRID
TENNESSEE
CARUTHERSVILLE
BLYTHEVILLE
MEMPHIS
ARKANSAS R.
HELENA
TENNESSEE R.
ROSEDALE
GREENVILLE
ARKANSAS
ALABAMA
LAKE PROVIDENCE
LA.
OUACHITA R.
MISSISSIPPI
RED R.
VICKSBURG
NATCHEZ
FLORIDA
SUGAR
LOUISIANA
BATON ROUGE
GRAMERCY
PLAQUEMINE
DONALDSONVILLE
HARVEY
NEW ORLEANS

MISSISSIPPI RIVER (Consolidated)

The Mississippi River rises in northern Minnesota and flows in a southerly direction to the Gulf of Mexico. Navigation extends from Minneapolis, Minnesota to the mouth of the Passes.

Total Mileage—2,360

Navigation Mileage—1,837

Project Depth—9 feet to 40 feet

Project Width—300 feet to 1,100 feet

Lock Dimensions—56′ by 400′—110′ by 600′ —110′ by 1,200′ (30 locks and dams)

Authorizations—
Original project—1824
Existing project—1928
Cost—$1,800,000,000 [1]

Yearly Average Cost of Operation and Maintenance —$22,800,000 (5 year average)

Navigation Season—Minneapolis to mouth of the Missouri: End of March through first week in December

Mouth of Missouri to Head of Passes —12 months

Major Types of Industries Located on Waterway

Chemical plants	Terminal facilities
Petroleum facilities	Sugar cane processing plant
Grain elevators	Power plants
Iron and steel mills	Aluminum plants
Cement plants	

Inland Waterway

The five principal commodities that make up 75 percent of the total traffic on the waterway are: petroleum and petroleum products; grain and grain products; bituminous coal and lignite; sand, gravel, crushed rock; and iron and steel products.

Oceangoing

The five principal commodities that make up 80 percent of the total traffic on the waterway are: petroleum and petroleum products; grain and grain products; aluminum ores, concentrates and scrap; soybeans; and liquid and dry sulphur.

[1] Federal cost of the Mississippi River and Tributaries project.

UPPER MISSISSIPPI RIVER

Navigation on the Upper Mississippi River starts at Minneapolis, Minnesota and flows southward to the mouth of the Missouri River, just north of St. Louis, Missouri.

Total Mileage—663

Project Depth—9 feet

Project Width—300 to 1,000 feet

Lock Dimensions—56′ by 400′—110′ by 600′ —110′ by 1,200′ (27 locks and dams)

Authorizations—
Original project—1878
Existing project—1930
Cost—$276,000,000

Yearly Average Cost of Operation and Maintenance —$10,700,000 (5 year average)

Navigation Season—9 months (end of March through first week in December)

Major Types of Industries Located on Waterway
- Chemical plants
- Warehouses, terminals and docks
- Grain elevators
- Petroleum facilities
- Iron and steel mills
- Paper plants
- Power plants
- Coal loading facilities
- Atomic Energy and nuclear plants
- Spacecraft plant

The five principal commodities that make up 80 percent of the total traffic on the waterway are: petroleum and petroleum products; grain and grain products; bituminous coal and lignite; sand, gravel, crushed rock; and iron and steel products.

McCLELLAN-KERR ARKANSAS RIVER NAVIGATION SYSTEM

The route follows the White River and the Arkansas Post Canal to the Arkansas River, flows up the Arkansas River to the mouth of the Verdigris River to Catoosa, Oklahoma.

Total Mileage—448

Project Depth—9 feet

Project Width—150 to 300 feet

Lock Dimensions—17 locks 110′ by 600′

Authorizations—

Original project—1832
Existing project—1938 and 1946
Cost—$1.2 Billion

Yearly Average Cost of Operation and Maintenance
$5,300,000 (5 year average)

Navigation Season—12 months

Major Types of Industries Located on Waterway—

Chemical
Lumber
Paper
Grain

The five principal commodities that make up 73 percent of the total traffic on the waterway are: Sand, gravel, crushed rock; soybeans; aluminum ores, concentrates; fertilizer and fertilizer materials; and aluminum ores, concentrates.

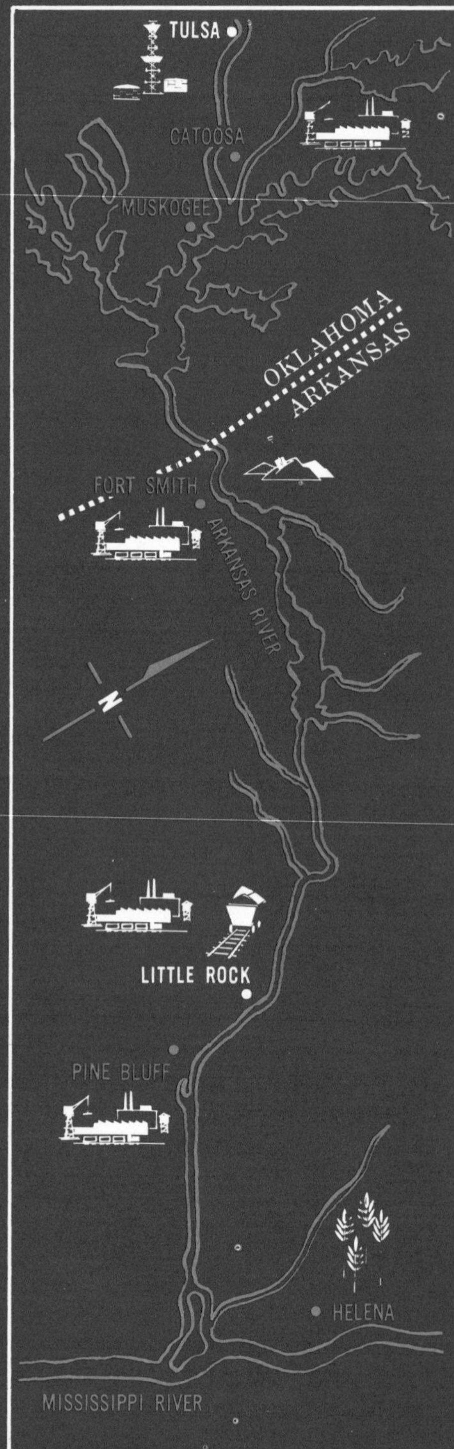

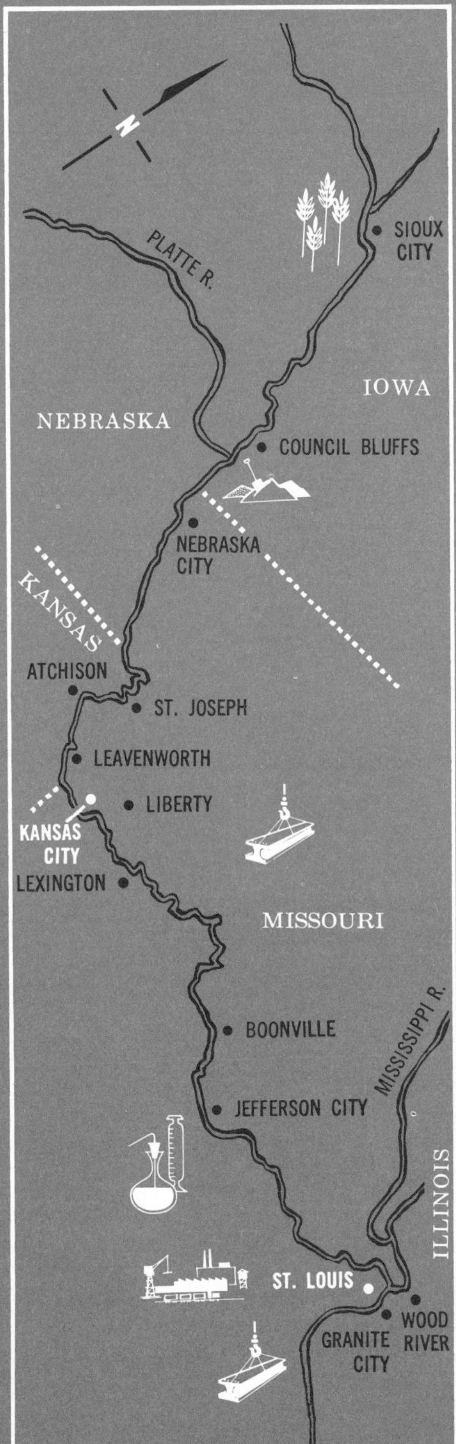

MISSOURI RIVER

The head of navigation on the Missouri River is Sioux City, Iowa flowing southeast to its confluence with the Mississippi River, 17 miles above St. Louis, Missouri.

Total Mileage—732

Project Depth—9 feet

Project Width 300 feet

Authorizations

Original project—1876
Existing project—1945
Cost $376,000,000

Yearly Average Cost of Operation and Maintenance
—$11,500,000 (5 year average)

Navigation Season—7½ months (April 1 through November 15)

Major Types of Industries Located on Waterway

Grain elevators and storage facilities
Chemical plants
Aluminum plants
Paint and varnish plant
Coal mines
Steel mills
Power plants
Cement plants

The five principal commodities that make up 90 percent of the traffic on the waterway are: grain and grain products; sand, gravel, crushed rock; soybeans; nonmetallic minerals and manufactures (not elsewhere classified); and petroleum and petroleum products. (Waterway improvement materials were excluded from these computations.)

ILLINOIS WATERWAY

The Illinois Waterway extends from Chicago Harbor at Lake Michigan to Grafton, Illinois and its confluence with the Mississippi River. In the Chicago area it includes the Calumet-Sag Channel and the Chicago Sanitary and Ship Canal.

Total Mileage—353.6

Project Depth—9 feet

Project Width—225 feet

Lock Dimensions—

Lockport	110′ by 600′
Brandon Road	110′ by 600′
Dresden Island	110′ by 600′
Marseilles	110′ by 600′
Starved Rock	110′ by 600′
Peoria	110′ by 600′
LaGrange	110′ by 600′

Note: The 1962 Authorization Bill provides for two new locks 110 feet by 1,000 feet, and modification of the project to provide for construction of supplemental locks, 110 feet by 1,200 feet, of the seven existing lock sites.

Authorizations—

Original project—1852
Existing project—1962
Estimated cost—$315,000,000

Yearly Average Cost of Operation and Maintenance —$3,600,000 (5 year average)

Navigation Season—12 months

Major Types of Industries Located on Waterways

Oil refineries	Sulphuric acid plant
Steel mills	Plastic products plant
Grain elevators	Power plants
Coal terminals	Atomic energy plants
Glass plants	Aluminum plants

The five principal commodities that make up 95 percent of the Great Lakes traffic on the waterway are: petroleum and petroleum products; fertilizer and fertilizer materials; grain and grain products; paper and paper products; and industrial chemicals.

The five principal commodities that make up 80 percent of the inland waterway traffic on the waterway are: bituminous coal and lignite; petroleum and petroleum products; grain and grain products; sand, gravel, crushed rock; and iron and steel products.

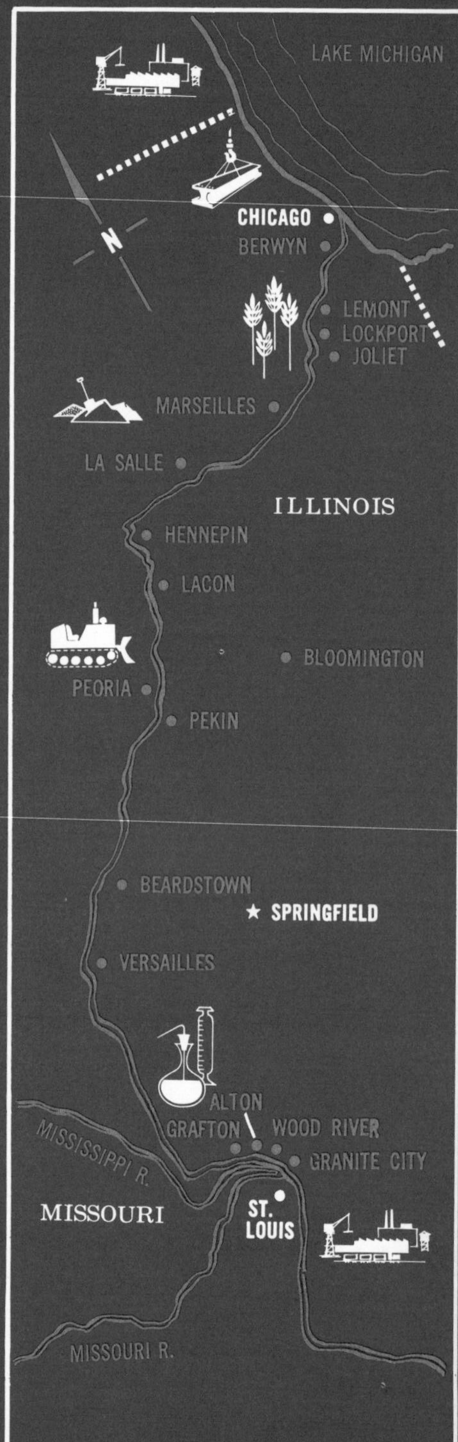

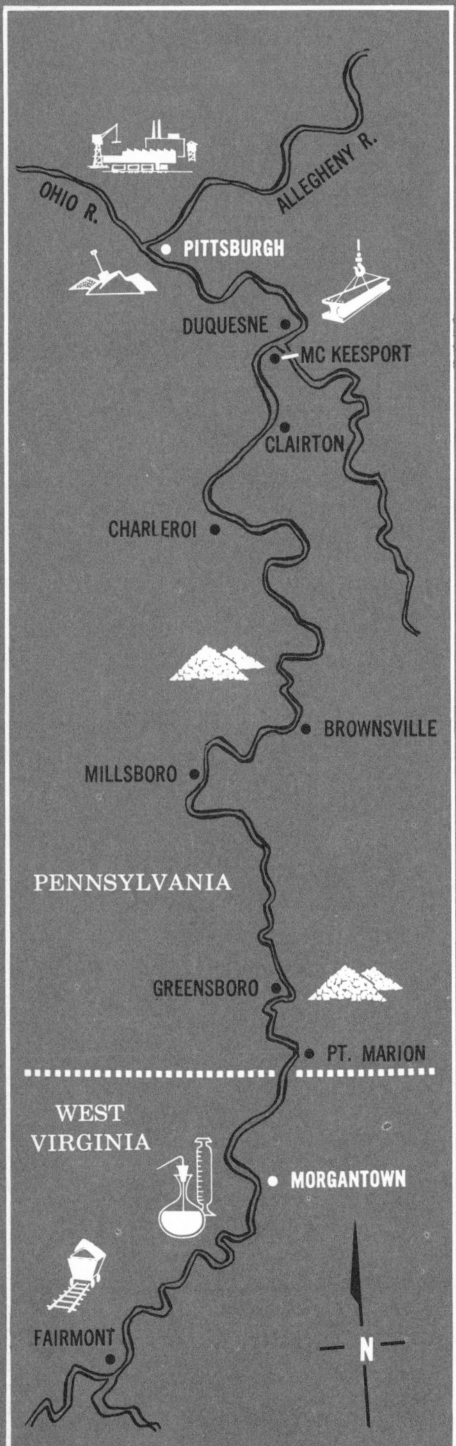

MONONGAHELA RIVER

The Monongahela River flows northwesterly from Fairmont, West Virginia to its confluence at Pittsburgh with the Allegheny River to form the Ohio River.

Total Mileage—129

Project Depth—7 to 9 feet

Project Width—300 feet

Lock Dimensions—

No. 2 (2 chambers)	56′ by 360′
	110′ by 720′
No. 3 (2 chambers)	56′ by 360′
	56′ by 720′
No. 4 (2 chambers)	56′ by 360′
	56′ by 720′
No. 5 (2 chambers)	56′ by 360′
No. 6 (2 chambers)	56′ by 360′
No. 7	56′ by 360′
No. 8	56′ by 360′
No. 14	56′ by 182′
No. 15	56′ by 182′
Maxwell	84′ by 720′
(To replace No. 4)	
Morgantown	84′ by 600′
Hildebrand	84′ by 600′
Opeskiska	84′ by 600′
(To replace Nos. 14 and 15)	

Authorizations—
- Original project—1872
- Existing project—1950
- Cost $147,000,000

Yearly Average Cost of Operation and Maintenance
—$1,900,000 (5 year average)

Navigation Season—12 months

Major Types of Industries Located on Waterway
- Steel mills
- Chemical plants
- Power plants
- Glass plants
- Coal and coke companies

The five principal commodities that make up 95 percent of the total traffic on the waterway are: bituminous coal and lignite; iron and steel products; sand, gravel, crushed rock; petroleum and petroleum products; and coal-tar products.

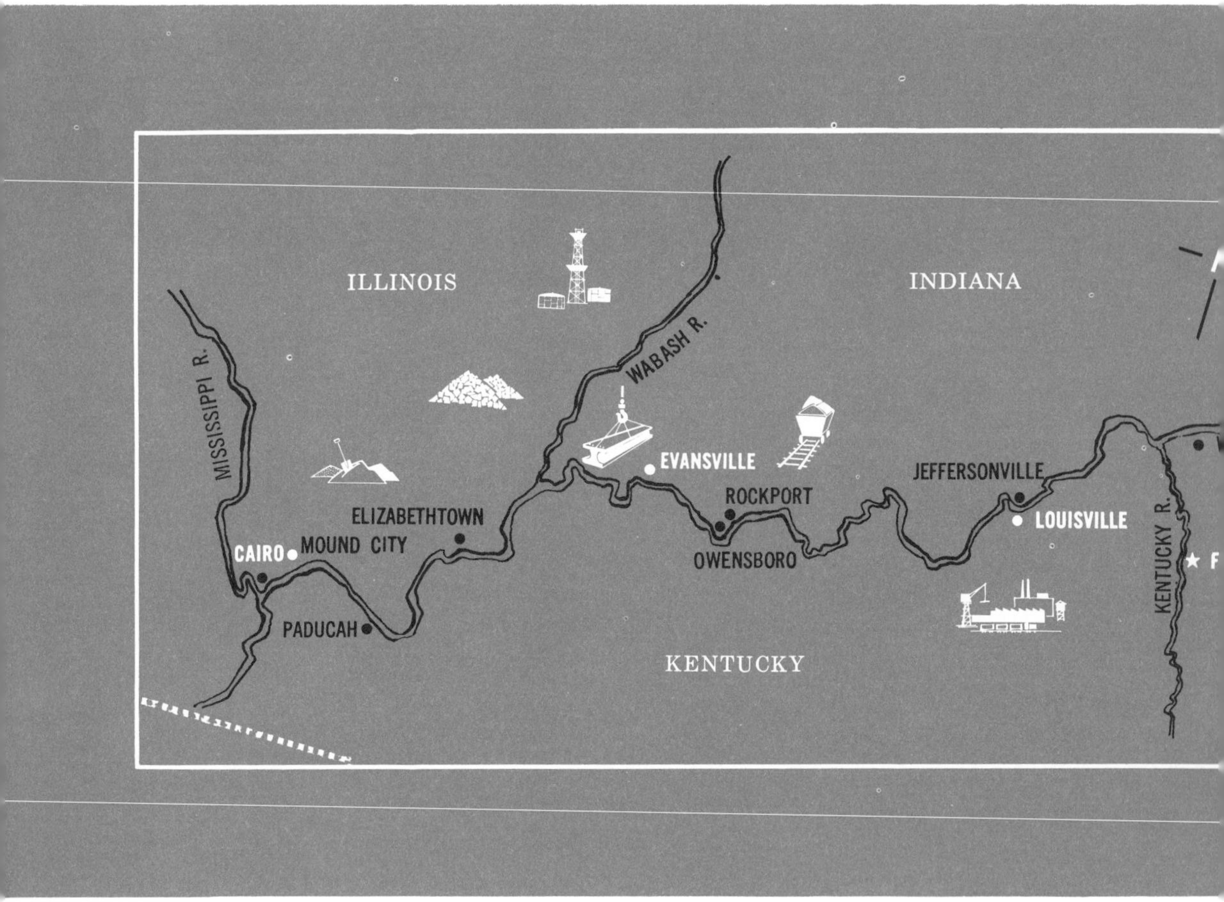

OHIO RIVER

The Ohio River is formed at Pittsburgh by the junction of the Allegheny and Monongahela Rivers and flows southwesterly to Cairo, Illinois, and its confluence with the Mississippi River.

Total Mileage—981

Project Depth—9 feet

Project Width—400 to 600 feet

Lock Dimensions—
43 existing—110′ by 600′ to be replaced by 19 locks—110′ by 1,200′

Authorizations—
Original project—1824—Cost $75,000
Existing project—1910—Cost $927,000,000

Yearly Average Cost of Operation and Maintenance—$10,700,000 (5 year average)

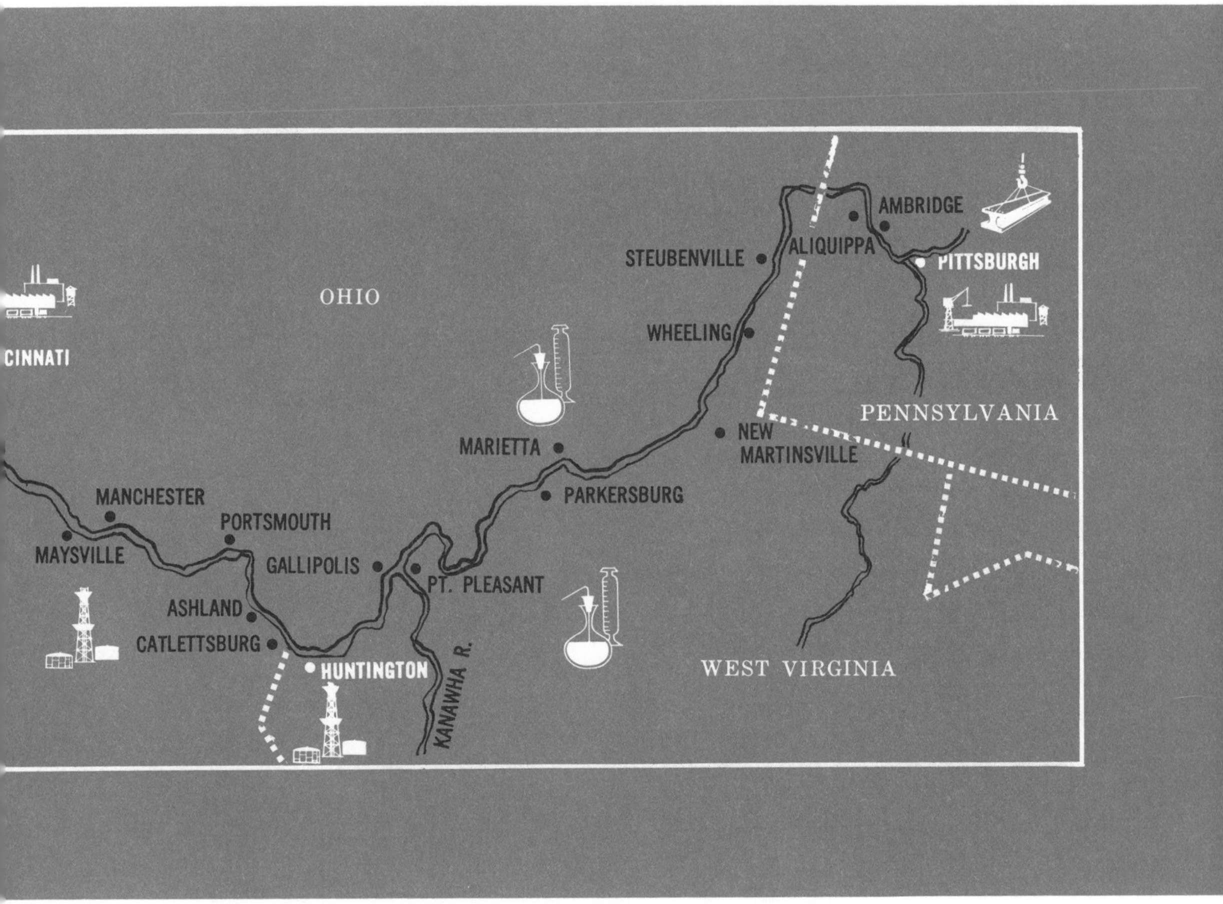

Navigation Season—12 months

Major Types of Industries Located on Waterway—

- Steel mills
- Glass plants
- Chemical companies
- Shipyards
- Oil terminals and refineries
- Power plants
- Lumber mills
- Coal companies
- Sand and gravel companies
- Grain elevators
- Aluminum fabricating plant
- Sulphur company

The five principal commodities that make up 85 percent of the traffic on the waterway are: bituminous coal and lignite; petroleum and petroleum products; sand, gravel, crushed rock; industrial chemicals; and crushed limestone.

ALLEGHENY RIVER

Navigation on the Allegheny River begins at East Brady, Pennsylvania southwestward to Pittsburgh and its confluence with the Monongahela River to form the Ohio River.

Total Mileage—72

Project Depth—9 Feet

Project Width—200 Feet

Lock Dimensions—56′ by 360′ (9 Locks)

Authorizations—
Original project—1886
Existing project—1934
Cost—$18,000,000

Yearly Average Cost of Operation and Maintenance
—$800,000 (5 year average)

Navigation Season—12 months

Major Types of Industries Located on Waterway
Steel mills
Coal mines
Cement plants
Paper plants
Plastics plants
Glass plant
Power plants
Industrial gas plant

The five principal commodities that make up 95 percent of the traffic on the waterway are: bituminous coal and lignite; sand, gravel, crushed rock; petroleum and petroleum products; iron and steel products; and ferroalloys, ores, metals (not elsewhere classified).

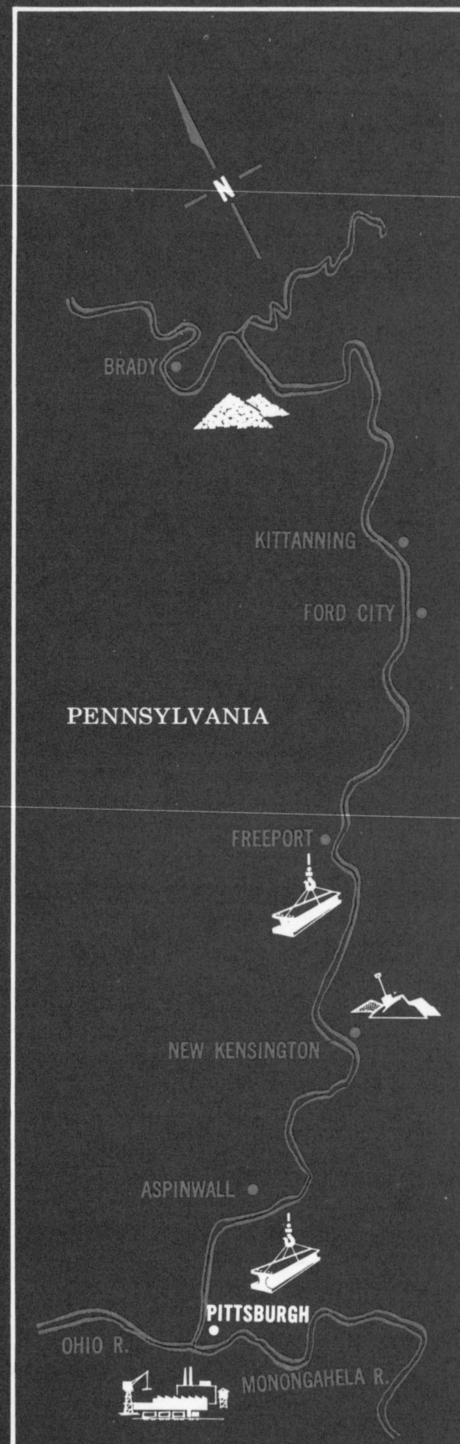

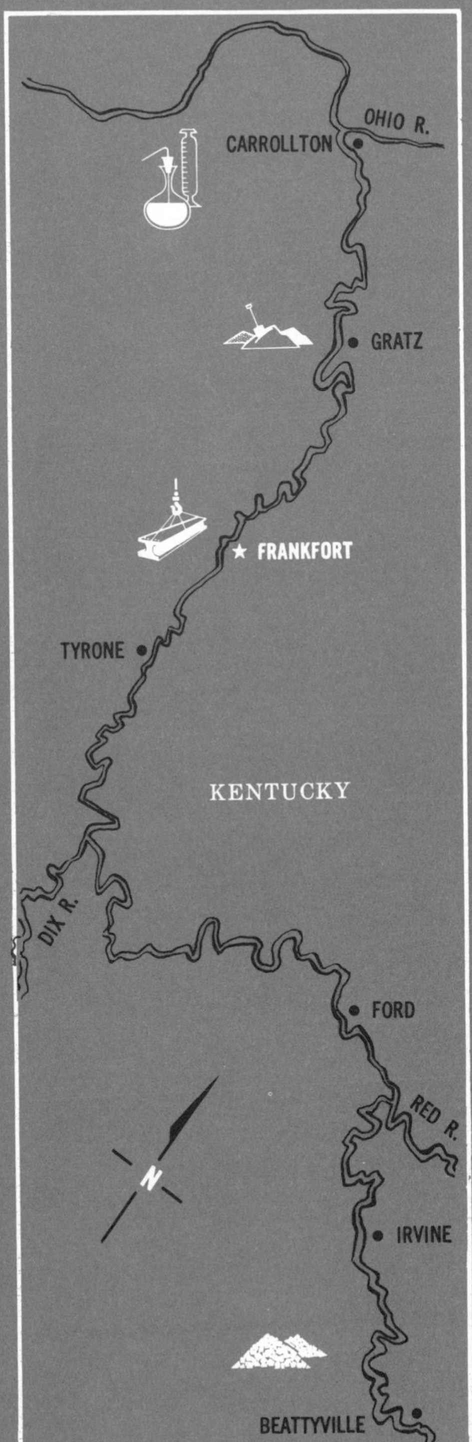

KENTUCKY RIVER

The Kentucky River is formed by the junction of the North and Middle Forks east of Beattysville, Kentucky, flows northwesterly to join the Ohio River at Carrollton, Kentucky.

Total Mileage—258.6

Project Depth—6 feet

Project Width—100 feet

Lock Dimensions—

5 Locks	38′ by 145′
2 Locks	52′ by 147′
1 Lock	52′ by 146′
6 Locks	52′ by 148′

Authorization—
1879
Cost—$4,200,000

Yearly Average Cost of Operation and Maintenance
—$873,000 (5 year average)

Navigation Season—12 months

Major Types of Industries Located on Waterway—
Coal loading facilities
Concrete plant
Power plants
Petroleum unloading facilities

Principal Commodities Transported on Waterway
Sand, gravel, crushed rock
Bituminous coal and lignite
Petroleum and petroleum products

KANAWHA RIVER

Navigation on the Kanawha River begins at Deepwater, West Virginia and flows northwestward to Point Pleasant, West Virginia and its confluence with the Ohio River.

Total Mileage—91

Project Depth—9 feet

Project Width—300 feet

Lock Dimensions—

London	56′ by 360′
Marmet	56′ by 360′
Winfield	56′ by 360′

Authorizations—

Original project—1873
Existing project—1930 and 1935
Cost—$23,000,000

Yearly Average Cost of Operation and Maintenance
—$981,000 (5 year average)

Navigation Season—12 months

Coal terminals
Chemical plants
Steel mills
Power plants
Synthetic rubber plant
Cement plant
Petroleum unloading stations

The five principal commodities that make up 90 percent of the total traffic on the waterway are: bituminous coal and lignite; industrial chemicals; sand, gravel, crushed rock; petroleum and petroleum products; and nonmetallic minerals and manufactures.

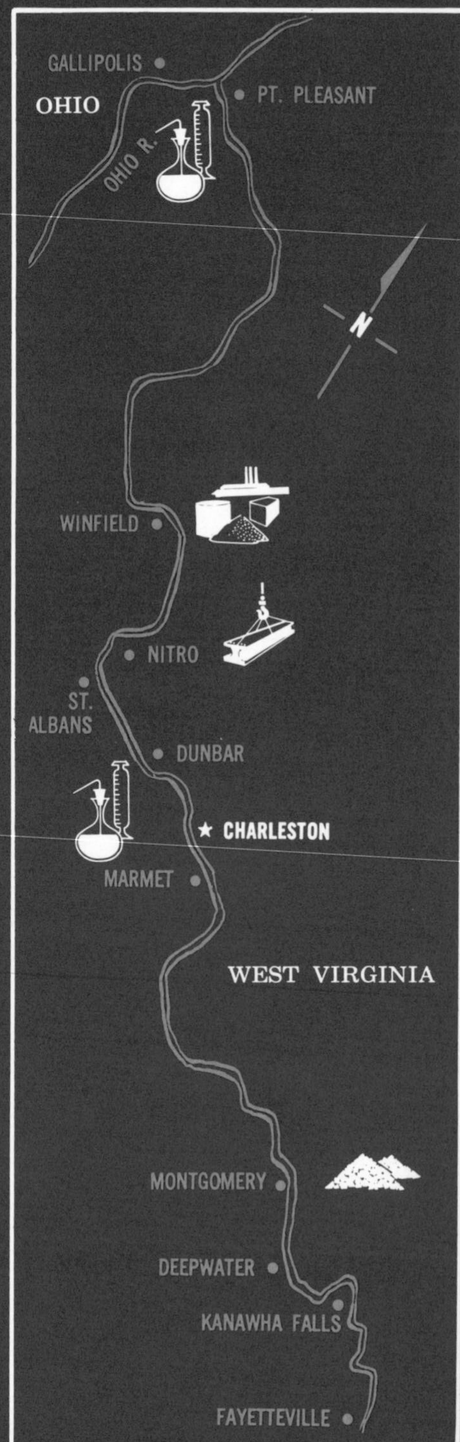

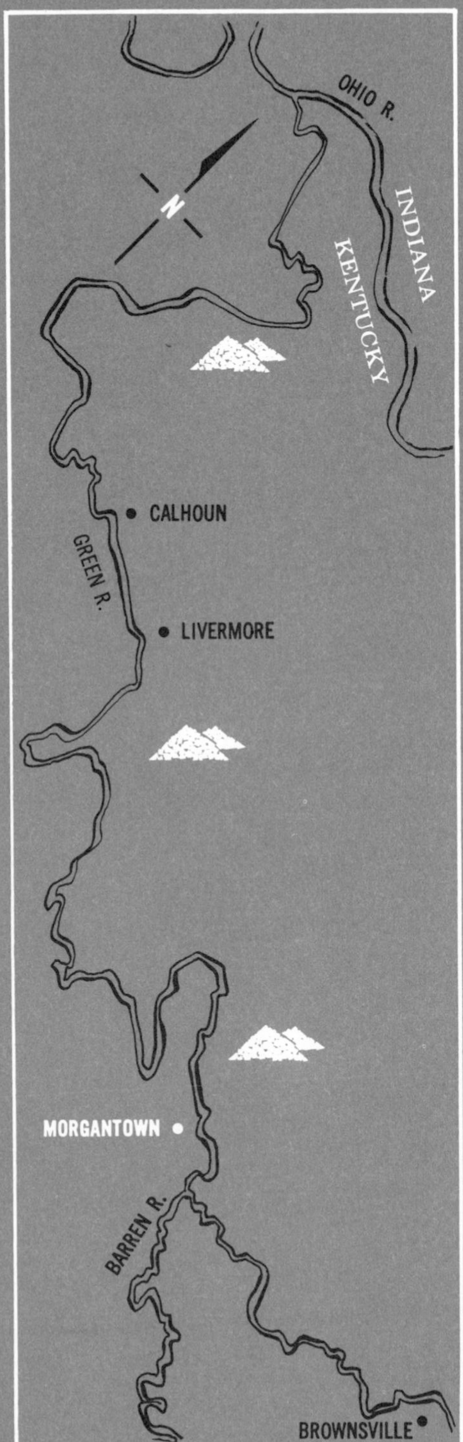

GREEN AND BARREN RIVER

The Barren River flows northwesterly from Bowling Green, Kentucky to its confluence with the Green River at Woodbury for a distance of 30 miles. The Green River flows northwesterly for a distance of 150 miles where it empties into the Ohio River eight miles above Evansville, Indiana.

Total Mileage—180

Project Depth—5.5 to 9 feet

Project Width—100 to 200 feet

Authorizations—
Original project—1888
Existing project
Cost—$14,000,000

Yearly Average Cost of Operation and Maintenance
$569,000 (5 year average)

Navigation Season—12 months

Lock Dimensions—

No. 1 Green River	84′ by 600′
No. 2 Green River	84′ by 600′
No. 3 Green River	35.8′ by 137.5′
No. 4 Green River	35.8′ by 138′
No. 1 Barren River	56′ by 360′

Major Types of Industries Located on Waterway—
Coal loading facilities
Power plants

Principal Commodities Transported on Waterway
Bituminous coal and lignite—over 99 percent
There are some petroleum products shipped over this waterway

TENNESSEE RIVER

The Tennessee River is formed at Knoxville, Tennessee by the junction of the Holston and French Rivers, flowing south and southwest to its confluence with the Ohio River at Paducah, Kentucky.

Total Mileage—652

Project Depth—9 feet

Project Width—300 to 500 feet

Lock Dimensions—

Kentucky	110′ by 600′
Pickwick	110′ by 600′
Wilson:	
Auxiliary	60′ by 292′
Main	110′ by 600′
Wheeler	60′ by 400′
Guntersville	60′ by 360′
Hales Bar	60′ by 265′
Chickamauga	60′ by 360′
Watts Bar	60′ by 360′
Fort Loudon	60′ by 360′

Authorizations—

Original project—1852

Existing project—1930

The Tennessee Valley Act of 1933 gave the TVA power to construct a project to provide a nine-foot channel and maintain a water supply from Knoxville to the mouth of the river.

Total Cost for Navigation—$136,000,000

Yearly Average Cost of Operation and Maintenance—$1,816,000 (5 year average)

Navigation Season—12 months

Major Types of Industries Located on Waterway—

- Oil Terminals
- Chemical plants
- Power plants
- Grain elevators
- Aluminum plants
- Paper mills
- Feed mills
- Cement plants

The five principal commodities that make up 75 percent of the total traffic on the waterway are: bituminous coal and lignite; sand, gravel, crushed rock; grain and grain products; petroleum and petroleum products; and crushed limestone.

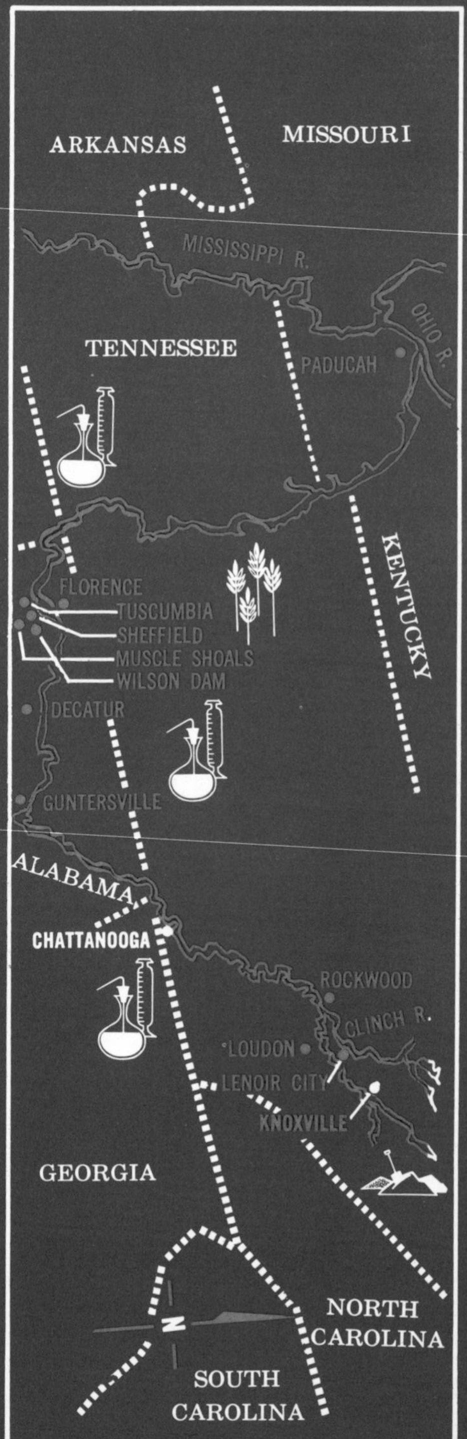

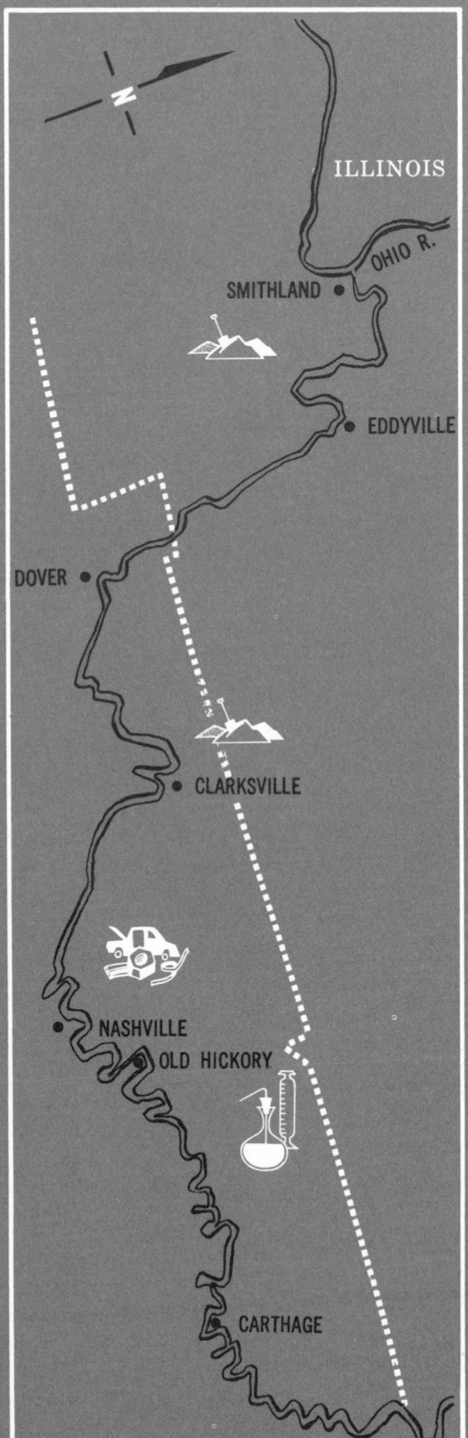

CUMBERLAND RIVER

Head of navigation on the Cumberland River is eight miles above Carthage, Tennessee, flows southward to Nashville, then northwestward to its confluence with the Ohio River at Smithland, Kentucky.

Total Mileage 317

Project Depth 9 feet

Lock Dimensions—

Barkley	110′ by 800′
Cheatham	110′ by 800′
Old Hickory	84′ by 400′

Authorizations—

Original project—1832
Existing project—1946
Cost—$175,000,000

Yearly Average Cost of Operation and Maintenance
—$3,160,000 (5 year average)

Navigation Season—12 months

Major Types of Industries Located on Waterway—

Cement plants
Chemical plants
Power plants
Fertilizer plant
Warehouses

The five principal commodities that make up 95 percent of the total traffic on the waterway are: petroleum and petroleum products; sand, gravel, crushed rock; iron and steel products; coal-tar products; and industrial chemicals.

BLACK WARRIOR, WARRIOR AND TOMBIGBEE RIVER SYSTEM

The Black Warrior-Tombigbee Waterway lies wholly within the State of Alabama and is made up of the Black Warrior, Warrior and Tombigbee Rivers, including the Sipsey, Mulberry and Locust Forks of the Black Warrior River.

Total Mileage—466

Project Depth—9 feet

Project Width—200 feet

Lock Dimensions—

Coffeeville	110′ by 600′
Demopolis	110′ by 600′
Warrior	110′ by 600′
Wm. Bacon Oliver	95′ by 460′
Holt	110′ by 600′
* John Hollis Bankhead	52′ by 286′

Authorizations—

Original project—1871
Existing project—1937
Cost—$105,000,000

Yearly Average Cost of Operation and Maintenance —$2,537,000 (5 year average)

Navigation Season—12 months

Major Types of Industries Located on Waterway—

- Coal mines
- Petroleum storage facilities
- Steel mills
- Steel fabrication plant
- Rayon mills
- Chemical plants
- Power plants
- Aluminum plant
- Paper mills

The five principal commodities that make up 80 percent of the total traffic on the waterway are: bituminous coal and lignite; petroleum and petroleum products; iron ore and concentrates; crushed limestone; and sand, gravel, crushed rock.

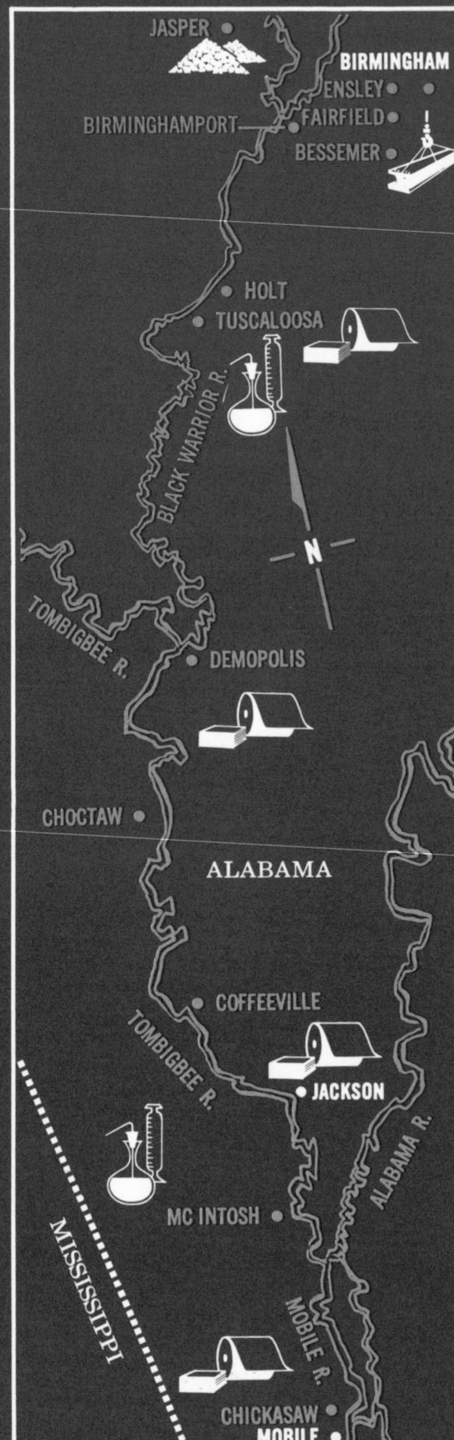

* New Replacement Lock (110′ x 600′) under construction. Lock scheduled for operation 1975.

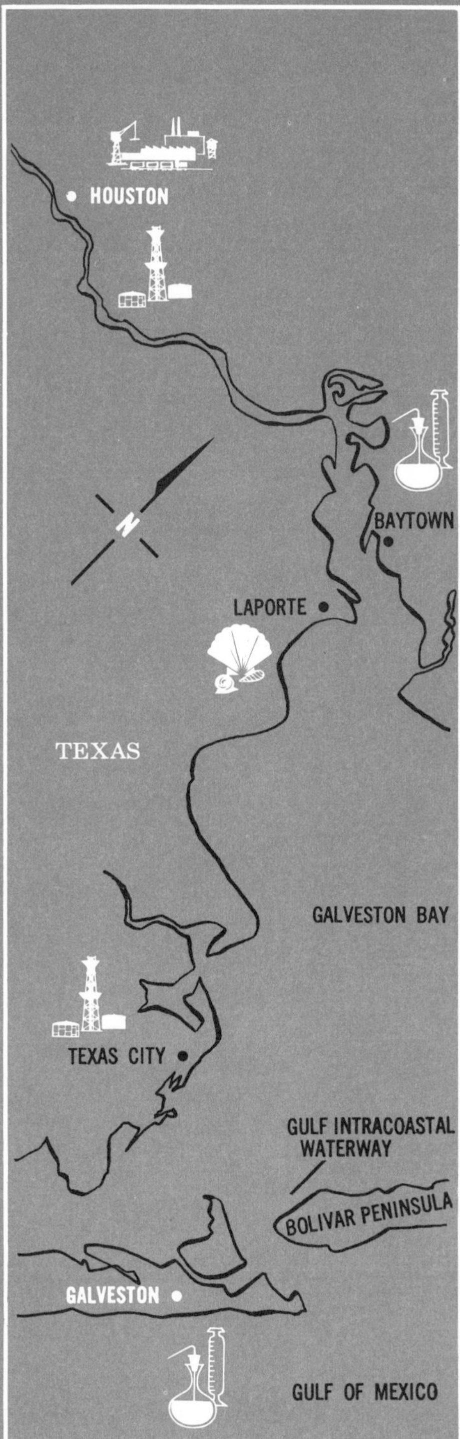

HOUSTON SHIP CHANNEL

The Houston Ship Channel connects Galveston Harbor opposite Port Bolivar with Houston, Texas, extending northwesterly across Galveston Bay through the San Jacinto River and Buffalo Bayou to a turning basin at Houston, Texas.

Total Mileage—50

Project Depths—8 to 40 feet

Project Widths—60 to 400 feet

Authorizations—
Original project—1872
Existing project—1958
Cost—$37,000,000

Yearly Average Cost of Operation and Maintenance
—$1,944,000 (5 year average)

Navigation Season—12 months

Major Types of Industries Located on Waterway—
Oil companies and terminals
Steel mills
Iron works
Chemical companies
Shipyard
Cement plants
Storage terminals

The five principal commodities that make up 85 percent of the total inland traffic on the waterway are: petroleum and petroleum products; unmanufactured sea shells; sulphuric acid; industrial chemicals; and coal-tar products.

The five principal commodities that make up 90 percent of the total ocean-going traffic on the waterway are: petroleum and petroleum products; grain and grain products; iron and steel products; fertilizer and fertilizer materials; and industrial chemicals.

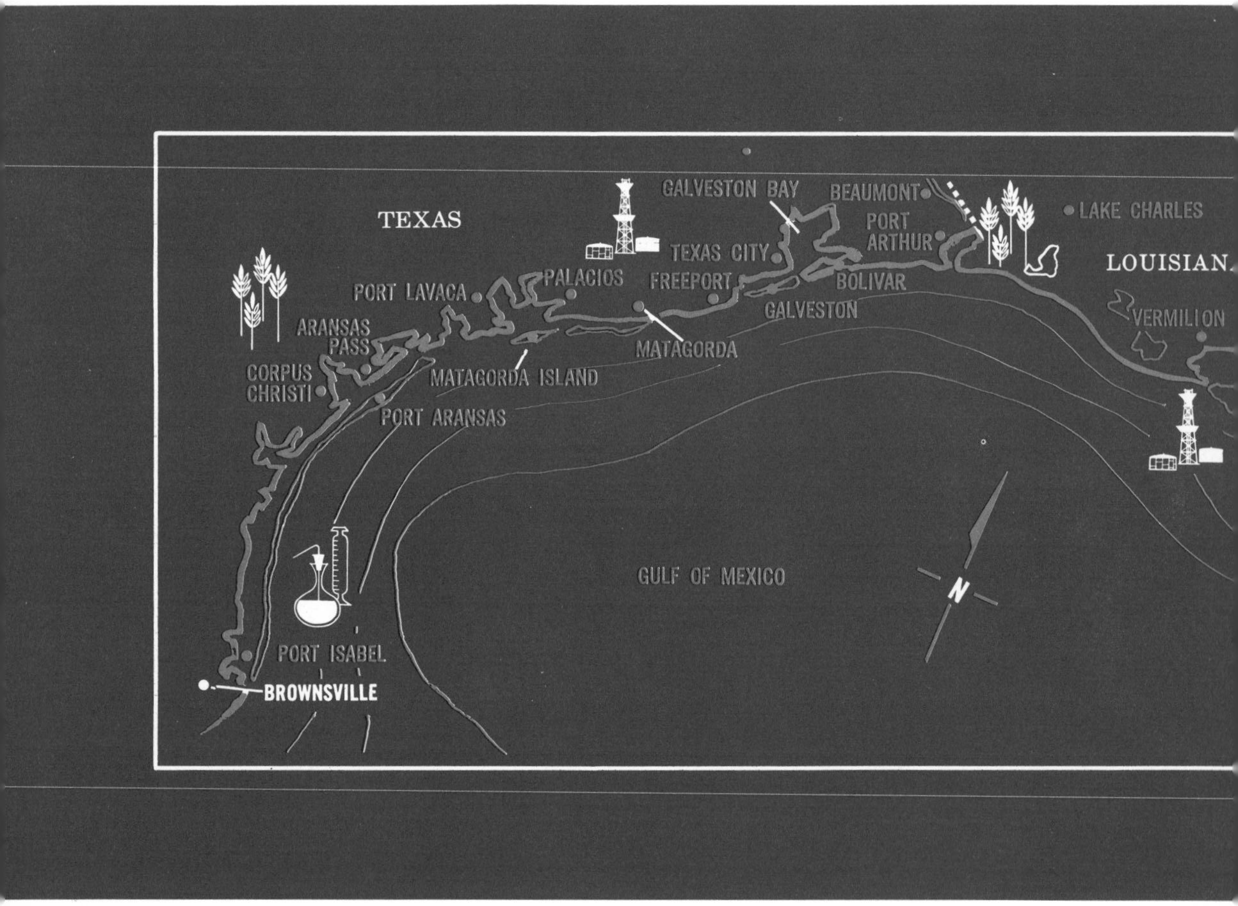

GULF INTRACOASTAL WATERWAY

The Gulf Intracoastal Waterway extends from Apalachee Bay (St. Marks), Florida to Brownsville, Texas.

Total Mileage—1,113

Project Depth—12 feet

Project Width—125 feet

Lock Dimensions—

Algiers	75′ by 760′
Bayou Boeuf	75′ by 1,160′
Bayou Sorrel	56′ by 760′
Calcasieu	75′ by 1,180′
Harvey	75′ by 425′
Port Allen	84′ by 1,200′
Old River	75′ by 1,200′
Vermilion	56′ by 1,182′
Inner Harbor	75′ by 640′

Authorizations—

Original project—1925

Estimated cost of construction—$137,-000,000

Navigation Season—12 months

Yearly Average Cost for Operation and Maintenance—$7,500,000 (5 year average)

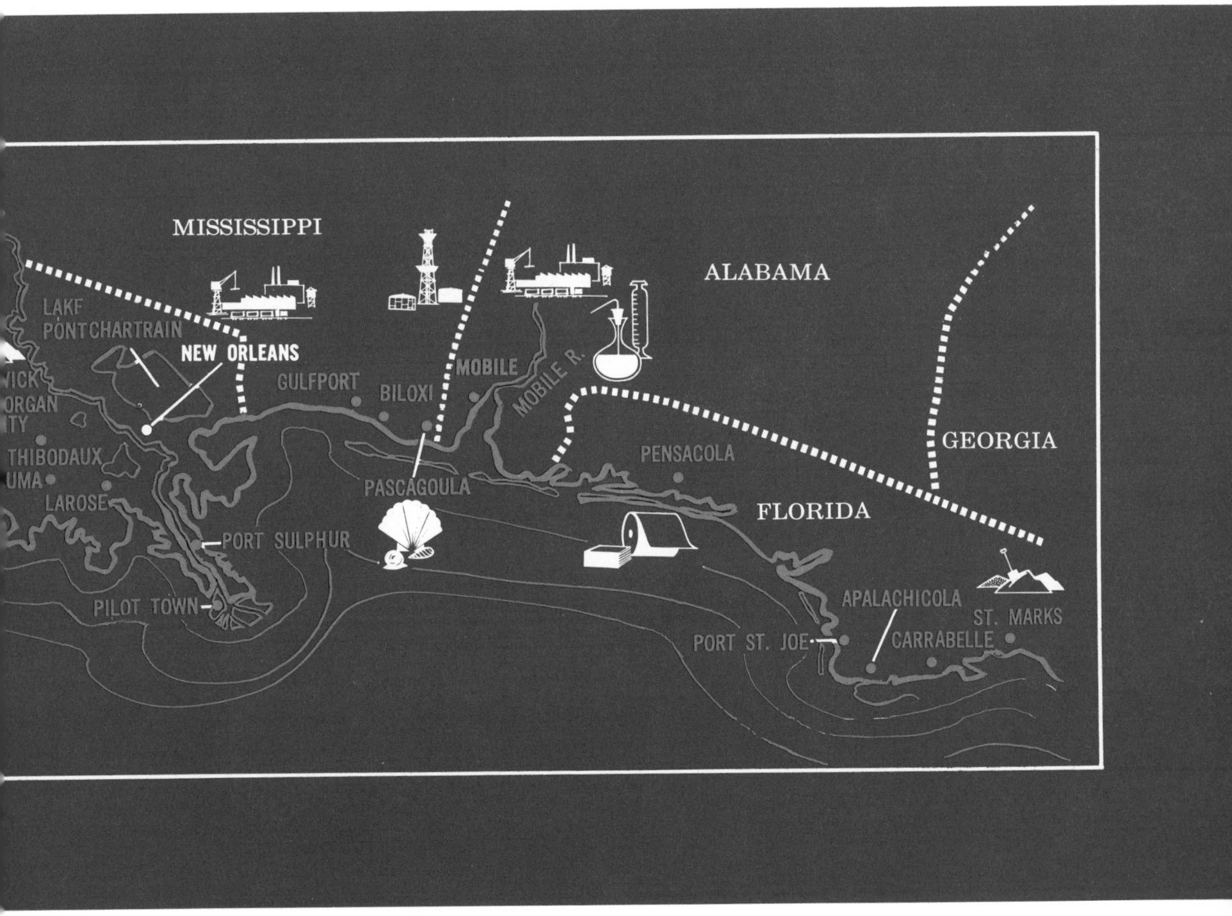

Major Types of Industries Located on Waterway—

Chemical plants
Glass plants
Paper mills
Oil refineries
Steel fabricating plants
Power plants
Shipyards
Fertilizer plant
Grain elevators
Synthetic rubber plant

The five principal commodities that make up 80 percent of the total traffic on the main route of the waterway are: petroleum and petroleum products; unmanufactured sea shells; industrial chemicals; iron and steel products; and nonmetallic minerals and manufactures.

The five principal commodities that make up 90 percent of the total traffic on the alternate route of the waterway are: petroleum and petroleum products; industrial chemicals; nonmetallic minerals and manufactures; unmanufactured sea shells; and coal-tar products.

APALACHICOLA, CHATTAHOOCHEE AND FLINT RIVER SYSTEM

The Apalachicola River from Apalachicola Bay to the confluence of the Chattahoochee and Flint Rivers, the Chattahoochee River to Columbus, Georgia (268 miles), and the Flint River to Bainbridge, Georgia (29 miles).

Total Mileage—297

Project Depth—9 feet

Project Width—100 feet

Lock Dimensions—

Jim Woodruff	82′ by 450′
Columbia	82′ by 450′
Walter F. George	82′ by 450′

Authorization—
Existing Project—1945
Cost—$306,717,000

Yearly Average Cost of Operation and Maintenance
—$4,079,000 (5 year average)

Navigation Season—12 months

Major Types of Industries Located on Waterway
- Chemical
- Warehouses
- Fertilizer
- Grain storage
- Lumber and products

Principal Commodities Transported on Waterway
- Petroleum and petroleum products
- Sand, gravel, crushed rock
- Dry sulphur
- Chemicals
- Sugar

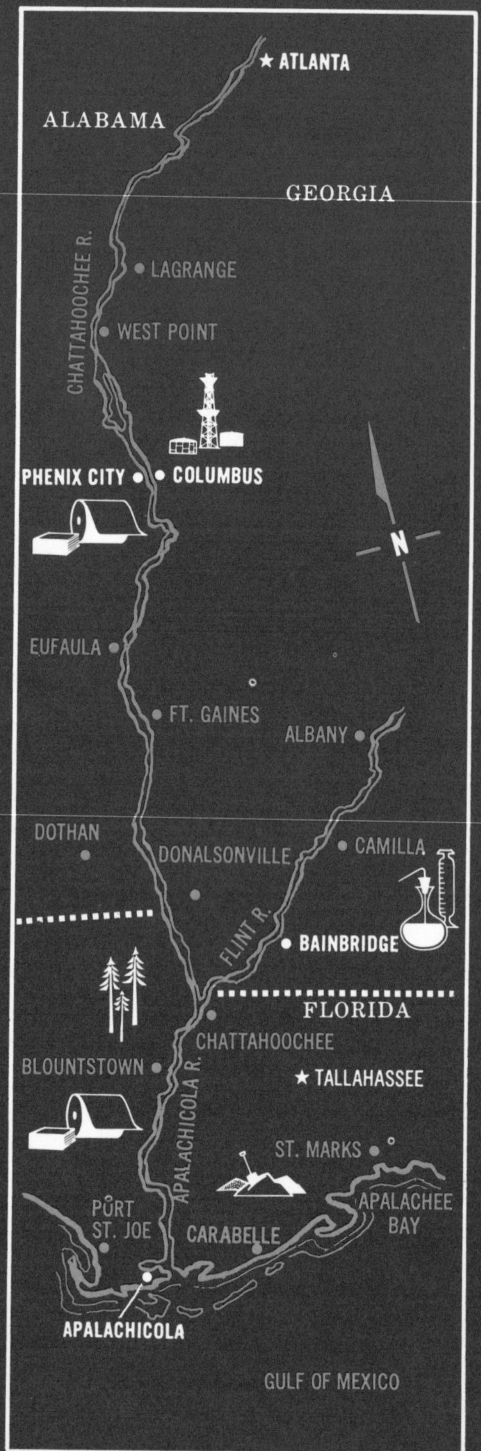

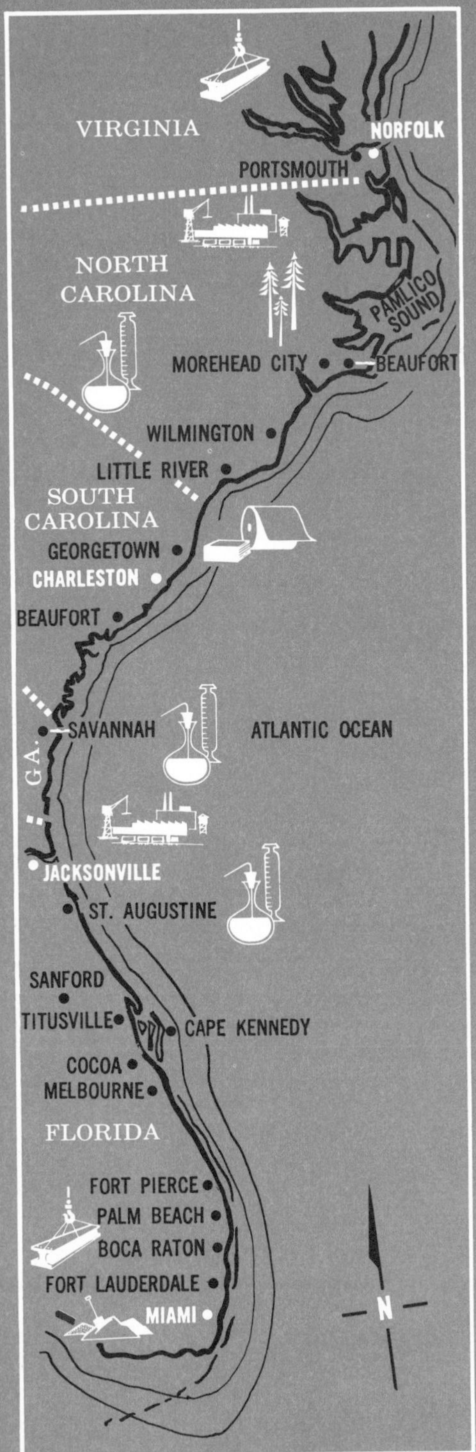

ATLANTIC INTRACOASTAL WATERWAY

The Atlantic Intracoastal Waterway extends from Norfolk, Virginia to Miami, Florida for purposes of navigation.

Total Mileage—1,129

Project Depth—12 feet

Project Width—90 feet

Lock Dimensions—

Great Bridge	75′ by 600′
Deep Creek	52′ by 300′

Authorizations—

George Washington made the first survey for the Dismal Swamp Canal in Virginia in 1755. It was opened in 1822.
Original project—1826
Existing project—1945 and 1954
Cost—$250,000,000 [1]

Yearly Average Cost of Operation and Maintenance
—$3,486,000 (5 year average)

Navigation Season—12 months

Major Types of Industries Located on Waterway—

Oil refineries
Paper mills
Cement plants
Chemical plants
Fertilizer plants
Sugar refinery
Grain elevators
Missile fuel and testing plant
Power plants

The five principal commodities that make up 75 percent of the total traffic on the waterway are: petroleum and petroleum products; woodpulp; pulpwood; fertilizer and fertilizer materials; and paper and manufactures.

[1] Section from Miami, Florida to Key West has been deferred for restudy.

DELAWARE RIVER

Navigation on the Delaware River begins at Trenton, New Jersey, flows south to the mouth of the Delaware Bay.

Total Mileage—129

Project Depth—12 to 40 feet

Project Widths—150 to 2,300 feet

Authorizations—
Original project—1872
Existing project—1954
Cost—$77,000,000

Yearly Average Cost of Operation and Maintenance
—$5,379,000 (5 year average)

12 months

Major Types of Industries Located on Waterway—
Chemical plants
Oil refineries
Steel products plant
Power plants
Glass plants
Plastics plant
Drydock and ship repair yards
Shipbuilding yards
Warehousing facilities
Sugar refinery
Storage terminals

The five principal commodities that make up 80 percent of the total inland traffic on the waterway are: petroleum and petroleum products; bituminous coal and lignite; sulphuric acid; gypsum or plaster rock; and woodpulp.

The five principal commodities that make up 90 percent of the total ocean-going traffic on the waterway are: petroleum and petroleum products; iron ore and concentrates; iron and steel products; sugar; and bituminous coal and lignite.

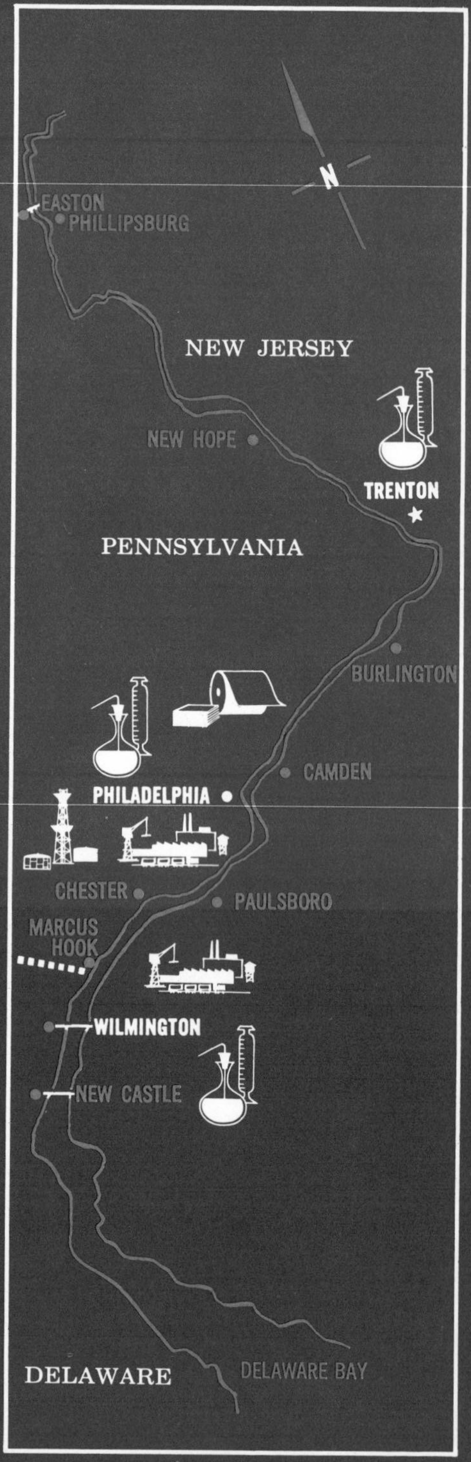

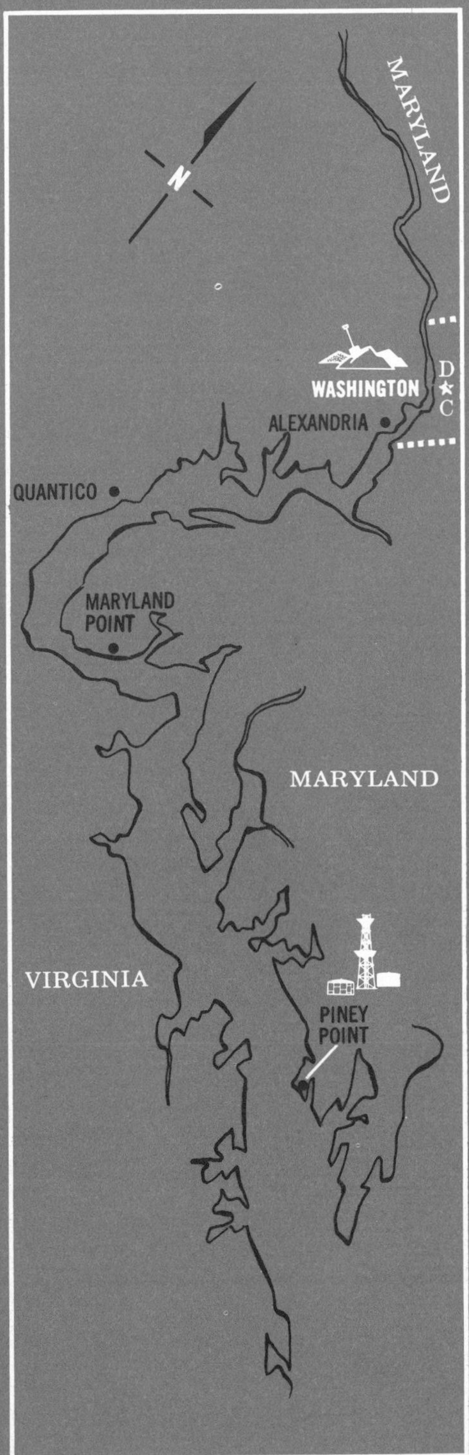

POTOMAC RIVER

Navigation on the Potomac River begins at Key Bridge, Washington, D. C. flowing in a southeasterly direction into the Chesapeake Bay, 80 miles from the Atlantic Ocean.

Total Mileage—113

Project Depth—24 feet

Project Width—200 feet

Authorization—1899

The existing $154,000 project was adopted in 1899 and completed in 1905.

Yearly Average Cost of Operation and Maintenance—$0 (5 year average)

Navigation Season—12 months

Major Types of Industries Located on Waterway—

Cement plants
Oil storage facilities
Flour mill
Terminals

The five principal commodities that make up 95 percent of the inland traffic on the waterway are: petroleum and petroleum products; sand, gravel, crushed rock; unmanufactured sea shells; shellfish and products; and fresh fish and products.

CHESAPEAKE BAY

The Chesapeake Bay flows south from Fort McHenry, Baltimore, Maryland to the Capes of Virginia to the Atlantic Ocean. (The C & D Canal on the north is the connecting link to the Delaware River.)

Total Mileage—200

Project Depth—42 feet

Project Width—1,000 feet

Authorization—
Existing project—1958

Yearly Average Cost of Operation and Maintenance
—$905,000 (5 year average)

Major Types of Industries Located on Waterway—
- Chemical plants
- Coke ovens
- Oil refineries
- Steel mills
- Shipyards

The five principal commodities that make up 90 percent of the total traffic on the waterway are: petroleum and petroleum products; bituminous coal and lignite; nonmetallic minerals and manufactures; iron and steel products; and fertilizers.

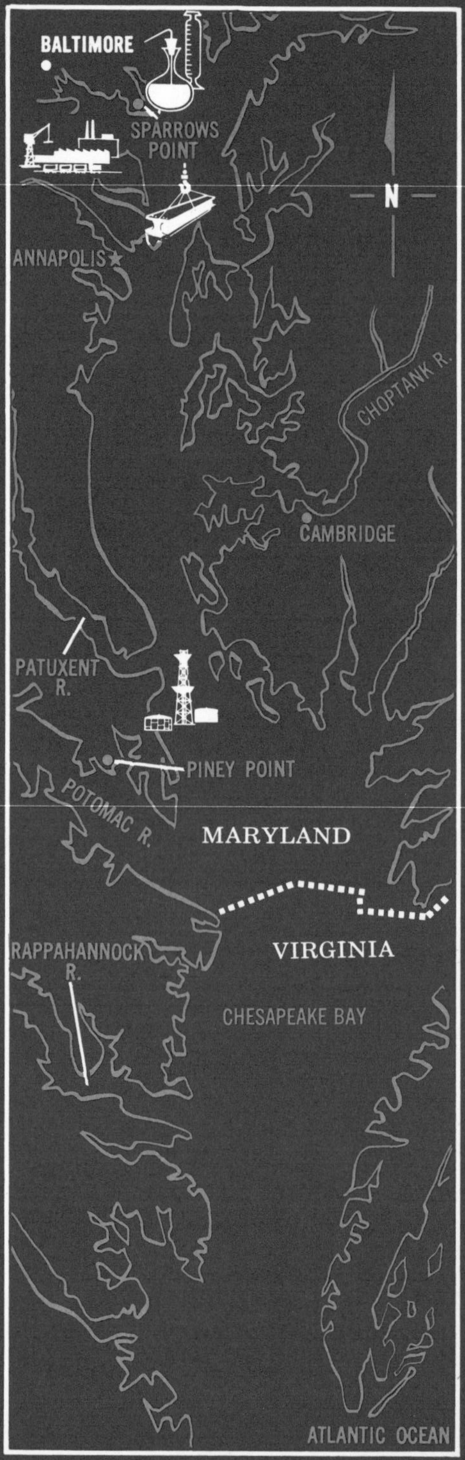

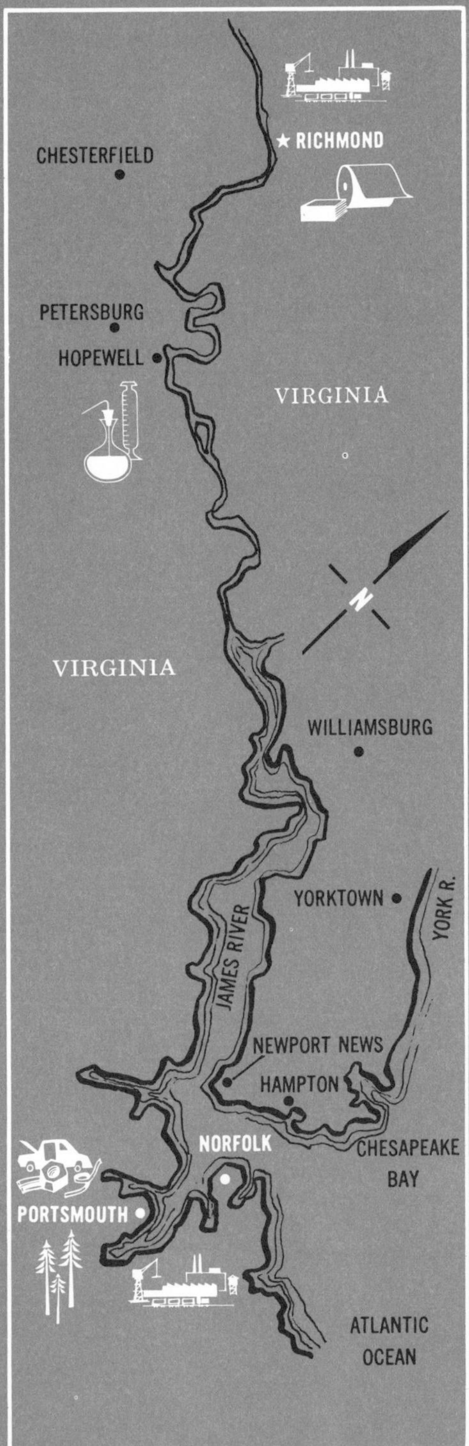

JAMES RIVER

Navigation on the James River extends from Richmond, Virginia to Hampton Roads at Newport News.

Total Mileage (Navigation)—89

Project Depth—18 to 35 feet

Project Width—200 to 300 feet

Authorization—1884
Existing project—1962
Cost—$47,196,000

Yearly Average Cost of Operation and Maintenance
—$441,200 (5 year average)

Navigation Season—12 months

Major Types of Industries Located on Waterway
Chemical
Lumber
Paper
Terminals
Scrap Metal

The five principal commodities that make up 95 percent of the total traffic on the waterway are: sand, gravel and crushed rock; petroleum and petroleum products; fertilizer and fertilizer materials; iron and steel scrap; and sulphuric acid.

HUDSON RIVER

The navigable section of the Hudson River extends from Waterford, New York south to New York City.

Total Mileage—155

Project Depths—14 to 32 feet

Project Widths—200 to 600 feet

Authorizations—
Original project—1834
Existing project—1954
Cost—$44,000,000

Yearly Average Cost of Operation and Maintenance
—$515,000 (5 year average)

Navigation Season—
Upper section, 8 months
Lower section, 12 months

Major Types of Industries Located on Waterway—
Steel corporations
Power plants
Atomic power plants
Chemical plants
Petroleum storage facilities
Cement plants
Marine terminals
Paper products plant

The five principal commodities that make up 80 percent of the total inland traffic on the waterway are: petroleum and petroleum products; sand, gravel, crushed rock; bituminous coal and lignite; crude oils, fats, waxes and vegetables; and brick and tile.

The five principal commodities that make up 60 percent of the total ocean-going traffic on the waterway are: petroleum and petroleum products; sand, gravel, crushed rock; bituminous coal and lignite; grain and grain products; and iron and steel products.

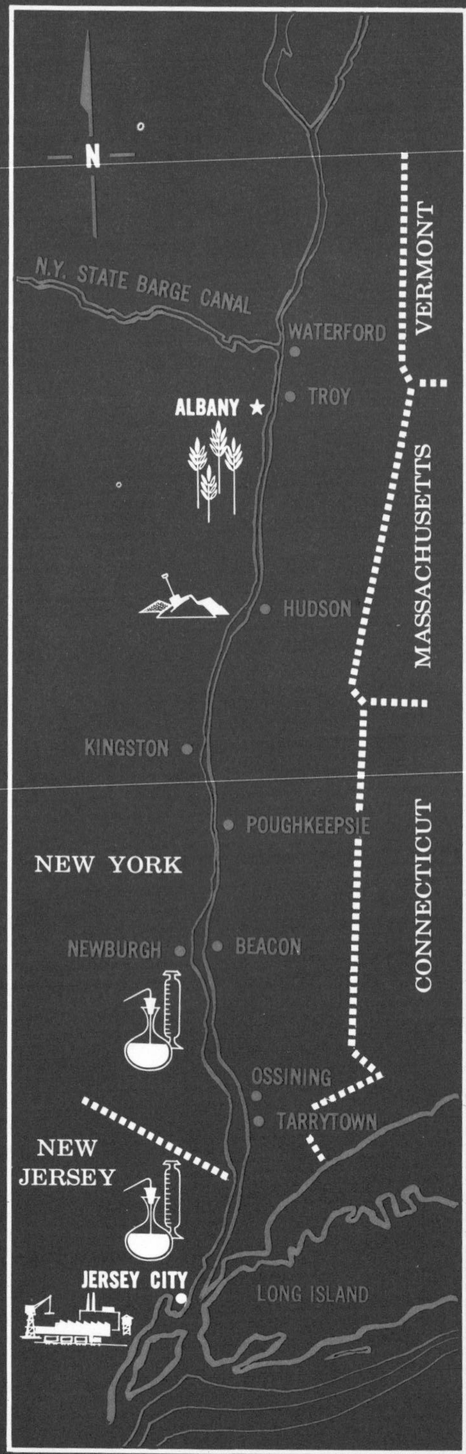

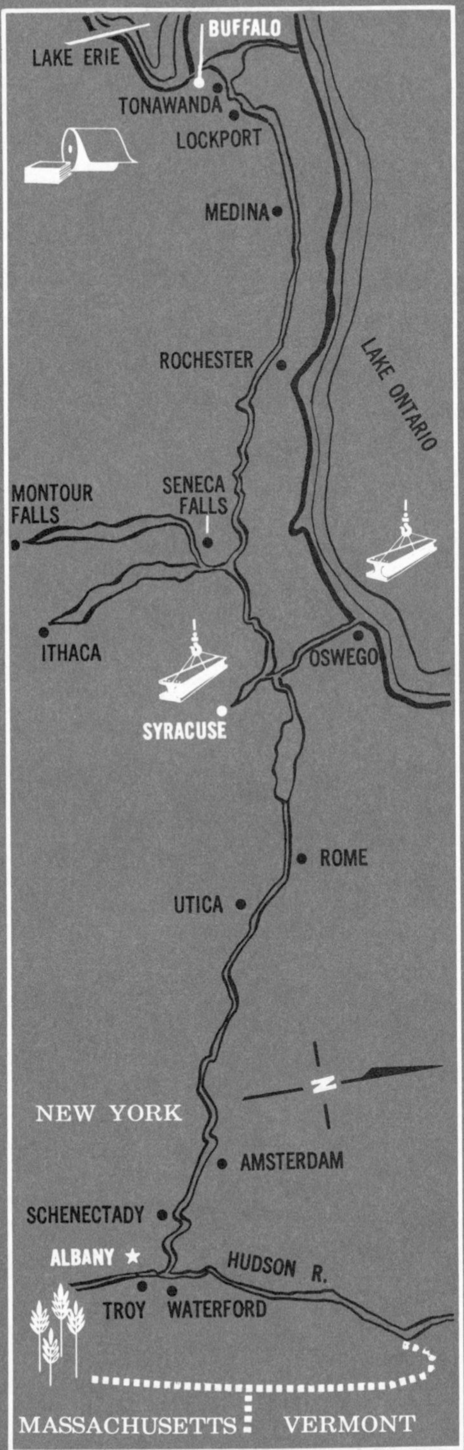

NEW YORK STATE BARGE CANAL

The New York State Barge Canal extends eastward from Niagara River at Tonawanda, New York to the Champlain Inlet at Whitehall, New York. The New York State Canal includes the Erie Canal (Waterford to Tonawanda), the Oswego Canal (Three River Point to Lake Ontario), the Cayuga-Seneca Canal (from the Erie Canal to Ithaca and Watkins including Cayuga and Seneca Lakes), and the Champlain Canal (Waterford to Whitehall), also canal harbors at Utica, Syracuse and Rochester.

Total Mileage—522

Project Depth—12 feet

Project Width—75 feet to 200 feet

New York State took over construction of the Canal in 1817; expansion of the present Canal was started in 1905. The Canal is a State owned and operated system.

Lock Dimensions—

There are a total of 58 locks on the Canal—45 feet by 300 feet

Erie Canal	36 Locks
Champlain Canal	11 Locks
Oswego Canal	7 Locks
Cayuga and Seneca Canals	4 Locks

Navigation Season—8 months (April to November inclusive)

Major Types of Industries Located on Waterway—

Grain elevators
Oil refineries
Chemical plants
Power plants
Steel mills

The five principal commodities that make up 85 percent of the total traffic on the waterway are: petroleum and petroleum products; industrial chemicals; inedible molasses; pig iron; and iron and steel scrap.

COLUMBIA RIVER

Navigation on the Columbia River starts at the bar and extends 340 miles to the tri-cities of Kennewick, Pasco and Richland, Washington. On the Snake River head of navigation extends to Lewiston, Idaho, mile 140.5. The head of navigation on the Willamette River is Corvallis, Oregon, mile 132.

Total Mileage(Navigation)—670

Project Depth—7 to 42 feet

Project Width—300 feet to 2,640 feet

Lock Dimensions—

Bonneville	75′ by 500′
The Dalles	86′ by 675′
McNary	86′ by 675′
John Day	86′ by 675′
Ice Harbor	86′ by 675′
Lower Monumental	86′ by 675′
Little Goose	86′ by 675′
Lower Granite	86′ by 675′

Authorizations—

Original project—1879
Existing project—1950
Cost—$1,000,000,000

Yearly Average Cost of Operation and Maintenance—$6,481,000 (locks and dams)

Navigation Season—12 months

Major Types of Industries Located on Waterway—

- Chemical plants
- Aluminum plants
- Oil-packaging plants
- Power plants
- Livestock feeds
- Oil refinery
- Lumber mills
- Pulp and paper mills
- Ship repair yards
- Grain elevators

The five principal commodities that make up 80 percent of the total inland traffic on the waterway are: petroleum and petroleum products; chemicals; fertilizers; rafted logs; grain and grain products; sand, gravel, crushed rock; and iron and steel products.

The five principal commodities that make up 70 percent of the total ocean-going traffic on the waterway are: grain and grain products; chemicals; lumber and shingles; petroleum and petroleum products; sand, gravel, crushed rock; and salt.

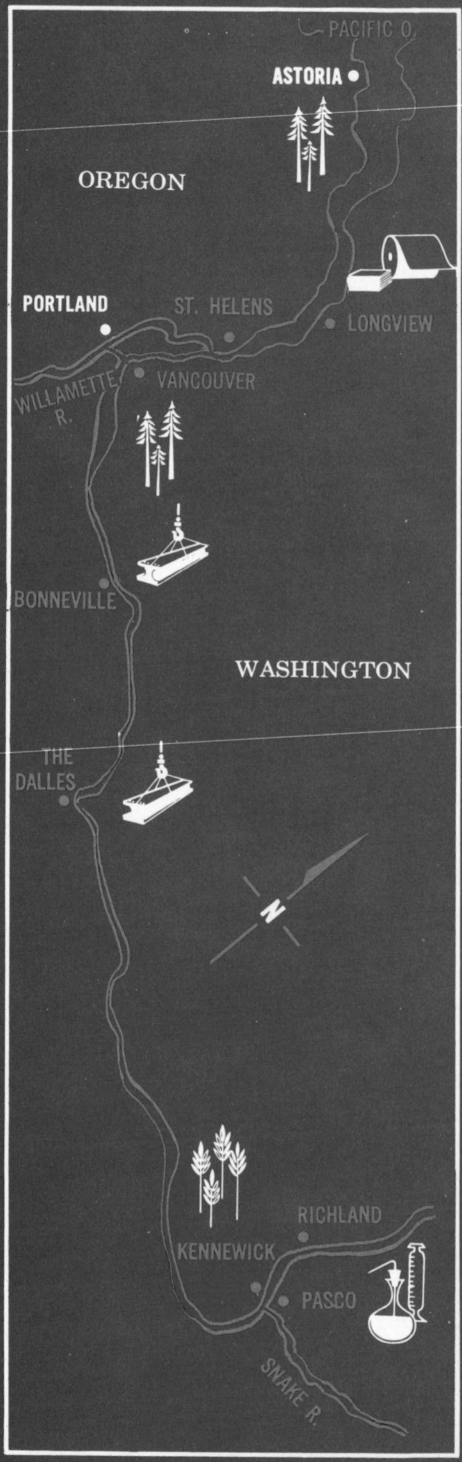

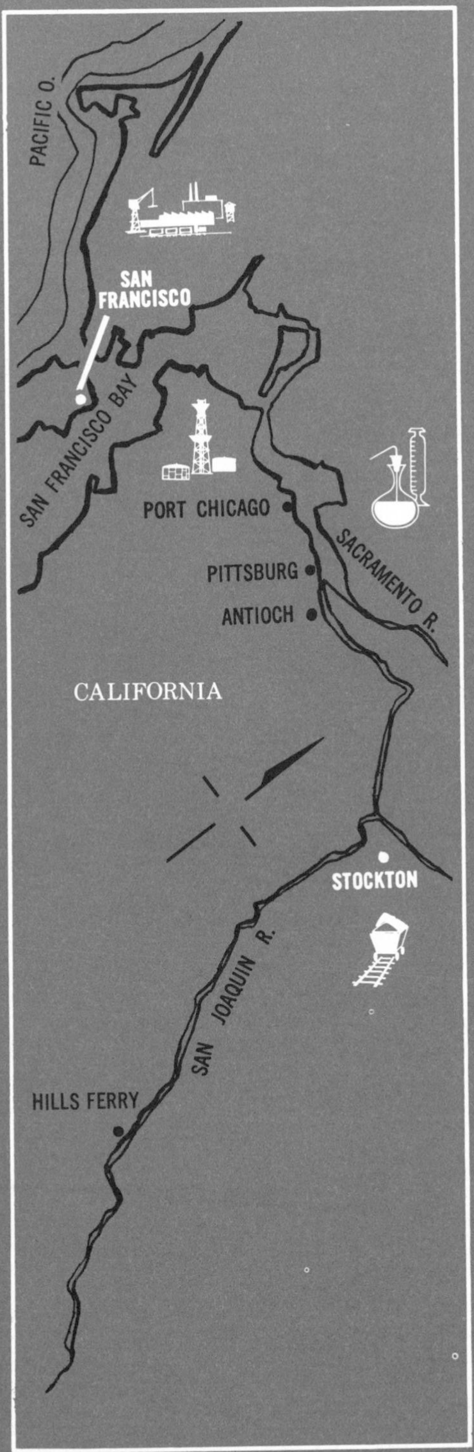

SAN JOAQUIN RIVER

The San Joaquin River rises in east-central California in the Sierra Nevada and flows southwesterly to the town of Mendota, then north to its confluence with the Sacramento River about 48 miles northeast of San Francisco. Head of navigation is Hills Ferry.

Total Mileage (Navigation)—127

Project Depth—

Project Width—225 to 400 feet

Authorizations—
- Original project—1876
- Existing project—1950
- Cost—$15,000,000

Yearly Average Cost of Operation and Maintenance —$261,500 (5 year average)

Navigation Season—12 months

Major Types of Industries Located on Waterway—
- Fertilizer plants
- Grain elevators
- Chemical plants
- Gypsum plants
- Packaging companies
- Feed mill and warehouse
- Paper products plants
- Berthing and storage facilities

The five principal commodities that make up 90 percent of the total inland traffic on the waterway are: petroleum and petroleum products; sand, gravel, crushed rock; grain and grain products; fresh vegetables and preparations; and fertilizer and fertilizer materials.

The five principal commodities that make up 70 percent of the total ocean-going traffic on the waterway are: iron ore and concentrates; grain and grain products; coke including petroleum coke; petroleum and petroleum products; and woodpulp.

SACRAMENTO RIVER

The Sacramento River rises in the Trinity Mountains in north-central California, flows generally south for about 374 miles to Suisun Bay. Head of navigation is near Colusa, California.

Total Mileage (Navigation)—145

Project Depth—6 to 10 feet

Project Width— 0 to 300 feet

Lock Dimensions—86′ by 600′ (1 lock)

Authorizations—
Original project—1899
Existing project—1946
Cost—$42,000,000

Yearly Average Cost of Operation and Maintenance
—$1,176,000 (5 year average)

Navigation Season—12 months

Major Types of Industries Located on Waterway—
Chemical plants
Gypsum companies
Warehouses and terminals
Power plants
Grain handling and processing plants
Tin plate mill

The five principal commodities that make up 95 percent of the total traffic on the waterway are: petroleum and petroleum products; grain and grain products; building cement; sand, gravel, crushed rock; and fresh vegetables and preparations.

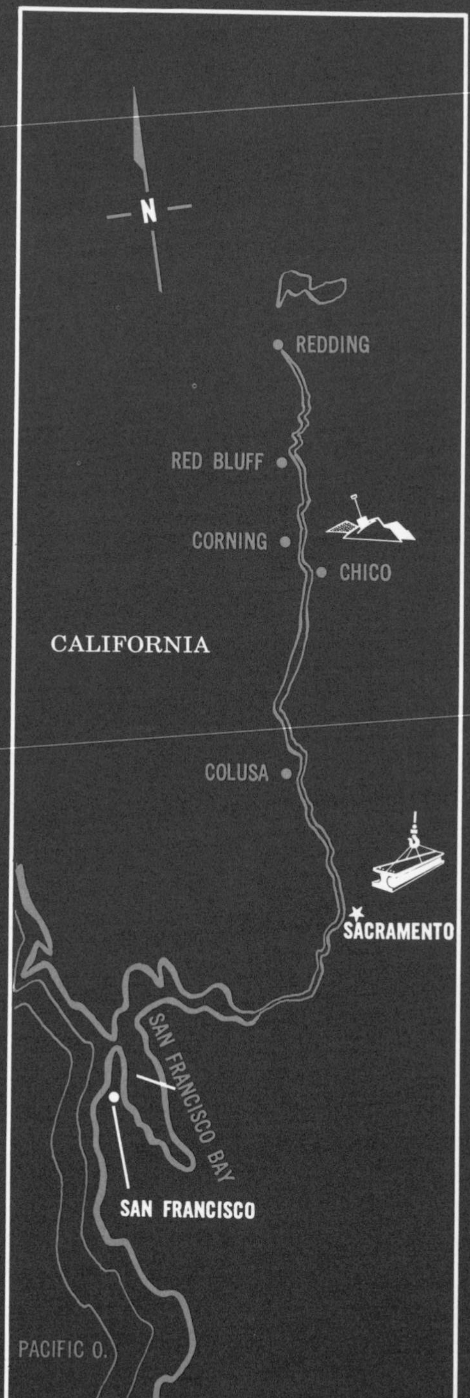

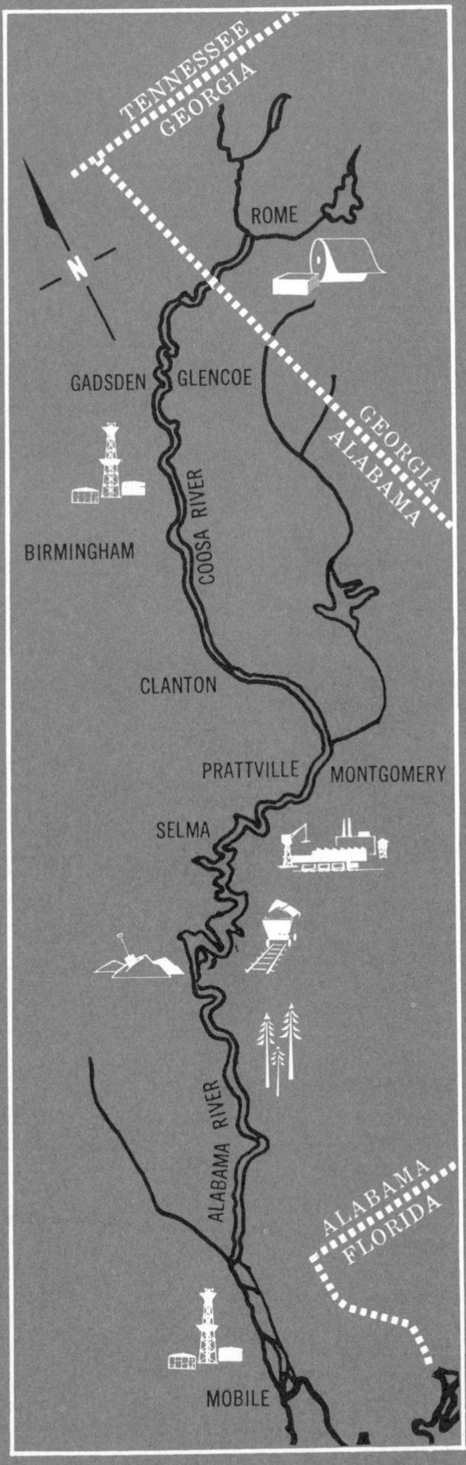

ALABAMA-COOSA RIVERS

The Alabama-Coosa River basin is part of the extensive Mobile River basin, which also includes the drainage areas of the Mobile, Tombigbee and Black Warrior Rivers. Its main streams are the Coosa, Tallapoosa and Alabama Rivers. Navigation and power on the Alabama and navigation on the Coosa are authorized Federal projects, with improvement of the Alabama funded and nearing completion.

Total Mileage—305.1 (existing project—junction with Coosa River)

Project Depth—9 feet

Project Width—200 feet

Lock Dimensions—

Claiborne	84′ by 600′
Millers Ferry	84′ by 600′
Jones Bluff	84′ by 600′

Authorizations—
Original project—1945
Existing project—1945
Cost—estimated $168,000,000 when completed in 1975.

Yearly Average Cost of Operation and Maintenance
—$719,263

Navigation Season—12 months

Major Types of Industries Located on Waterway
Paper mills
Petroleum storage facilities
Power Plants
Sand and gravel mining operations

Principal Commodities—
Sand and gravel
Wood and wood products
Petroleum and products
Miscellaneous

Mississippi river system

Upper Mississippi River and Tributaries[1]													Lower Mississippi River											
Minneapolis, Minnesota	LaCrosse, Wisconsin	Dubuque, Iowa	Rock Island, Illinois	Grafton, Illinois	St. Louis, Missouri	Cape Girardeau, Missouri	Chicago, Illinois	Joliet, Illinois	Peoria, Illinois	Omaha, Nebraska	Kansas City, Missouri	Jefferson City, Missouri	Cairo, Illinois	Memphis, Tennessee	Helena, Arkansas	Greenville, Mississippi	Vicksburg, Mississippi	Natchez, Mississippi	Baton Rouge, Louisiana	New Orleans, Louisiana	Pittsburgh, Pennsylvania	Ambridge, Pennsylvania	Wheeling, West Virginia	Parkersburg, West Virginia
155																								
274	119																							
371	216	97																						
635	480	361	264																					
673	518	399	302	38																				
801	646	527	430	166	128																			
956	801	682	585	321	359	487																		
923	768	649	552	288	326	454	33																	
798	643	521	427	163	201	329	159	126																
1274	1119	1000	903	639	631	750	960	927	801															
1024	869	750	653	389	382	510	710	677	551	250														
801	646	527	430	166	159	287	487	454	328	473	223													
855	700	581	484	220	182	54	541	508	382	813	563	340												
1084	929	810	713	449	411	283	770	737	611	1043	793	570	233											
1157	1002	883	786	522	484	356	843	810	684	1115	865	642	306	73										
1284	1129	1010	913	649	611	483	970	937	808	1242	992	769	433	200	127									
1385	1230	1111	1014	750	712	584	1071	1038	912	1344	1094	871	534	301	228	101								
1457	1302	1183	1086	822	784	656	1143	1110	984	1415	1165	942	606	373	300	173	72							
1589	1434	1315	1218	954	916	788	1275	1242	1116	1547	1297	1074	738	505	432	305	204	132						
1722	1567	1448	1351	1087	1049	921	1408	1375	1249	1680	1430	1207	871	638	565	438	337	265	133					
1834	1679	1560	1463	1199	1161	1033	1520	1487	1361	1792	1542	1319	979	1212	1285	1412	1513	1585	1717	1850				
1818	1663	1544	1447	1183	1145	1017	1504	1471	1345	1776	1526	1303	963	1196	1269	1396	1497	1569	1701	1834	16			
1744	1589	1470	1373	1109	1071	943	1430	1397	1271	1702	1452	1229	889	1122	1195	1322	1423	1495	1627	1760	91	75		
1650	1495	1376	1279	1015	977	849	1336	1303	1177	1608	1358	1135	795	1028	1101	1228	1329	1401	1533	1666	185	169	94	
1569	1414	1295	1198	934	896	768	1255	1222	1096	1527	1277	1054	714	947	1020	1147	1248	1320	1452	1585	265	249	174	80
1526	1371	1252	1155	891	853	725	1212	1179	1053	1484	1234	1011	671	904	977	1104	1205	1277	1409	1542	308	292	217	123
1511	1356	1237	1140	876	838	710	1220	1164	1039	1469	1219	996	656	889	962	1089	1190	1262	1394	1527	323	307	232	138
1364	1209	1090	993	729	691	563	1050	1017	891	1322	1072	849	509	742	815	942	1043	1115	1247	1380	470	454	379	285
1230	1075	956	859	595	557	429	916	883	757	1189	939	716	376	609	682	809	910	982	1114	1247	604	588	513	419
1078	923	804	707	443	405	277	764	731	605	1036	786	563	223	456	529	656	757	829	961	1094	757	741	666	572
1042	887	768	671	407	369	241	728	695	569	1000	750	527	187	420	493	620	721	793	925	1058	792	776	701	607
900	745	626	529	265	227	99	586	553	427	858	608	385	45	278	351	478	579	651	783	916	934	918	843	749
1961	1806	1687	1590	1326	1288	1160	1647	1614	1488	1919	1669	1446	1106	1339	1412	1539	1640	1712	1844	1977	127	143	218	312
1935	1780	1661	1564	1300	1262	1134	1621	1588	1462	1893	1643	1420	1080	1313	1386	1513	1614	1686	1818	1951	101	117	192	286
1890	1735	1616	1519	1255	1217	1089	1576	1543	1417	1848	1598	1375	1035	1268	1341	1468	1569	1641	1773	1906	56	72	147	241
1654	1499	1380	1283	1019	981	853	1340	1307	1181	1612	1362	1139	799	1032	1105	1232	1333	1405	1537	1670	350	334	259	165
1627	1472	1353	1256	992	954	826	1313	1280	1154	1585	1335	1112	772	1005	1078	1205	1306	1378	1510	1643	323	307	232	138
1601	1446	1327	1230	966	928	800	1287	1254	1128	1559	1309	1086	746	979	1052	1179	1280	1352	1484	1617	297	281	206	112
1114	959	840	743	479	441	313	800	767	641	1072	822	599	259	492	565	692	793	865	997	1130	848	832	757	663
1549	1394	1275	1178	914	876	748	1235	1202	1076	1507	1257	1034	694	927	1000	1127	1228	1300	1432	1565	1580	1564	1489	1395
1366	1211	1092	995	731	693	565	1052	1019	893	1324	1074	851	511	744	817	944	1045	1117	1249	1382	1397	1381	1306	1212
1259	1104	985	888	624	586	458	945	912	786	1218	968	745	404	637	710	837	938	1010	1142	1275	1291	1275	1200	1106
1206	1051	932	835	571	533	405	892	859	733	1164	914	691	351	584	657	784	885	957	1089	1222	1237	1221	1146	1052
1155	1000	881	784	520	482	354	841	808	682	1114	864	641	301	534	607	734	835	907	1039	1172	1187	1171	1096	1002
1222	1067	948	851	587	549	421	908	875	749	1180	930	707	367	600	673	800	901	973	1105	1238	1229	1213	1138	1044
1134	979	860	763	499	461	333	820	787	661	1092	842	619	279	512	585	712	813	885	1017	1150	1141	1125	1050	956
1105	950	831	734	470	432	304	791	758	632	1063	813	590	250	483	556	683	784	856	988	1121	1112	1096	1021	927
1040	885	766	669	405	367	239	726	693	568	998	748	525	185	418	491	618	719	791	923	1056	1047	1031	956	862
916	761	642	545	281	243	115	602	569	444	874	624	401	61	294	367	494	595	667	799	932	923	907	832	738

[1] Includes Illinois Waterway and Missouri River

[2] Monongahela, Kanawha, Green and Barren, Tennessee and Cumberland Rivers

Source: Light List—Volume V—United States Coast Guard

MISSISSIPPI RIVER SYSTEM

Distance Tables . . . . In Statute Miles

Distances on the McClellan-Kerr Arkansas River Navigation System

Mile Point From Mouth			Mile Point From Mouth		
007	White River Entrance	Ark.	106	David D. Terry Lock & Dam	Ark.
009	Arkansas Post Canal (White River)	Ark.	117	Little Rock	Ark.
010	Lock & Dam 1	Ark.	123	Lock & Dam No. 7	Ark.
013	Lock No. 2	Ark.	153	Lock & Dam No. 8	Ark.
019	Arkansas Post Canal (Arkansas River)	Ark.	173	Lock & Dam No. 9	Ark.
023	Pendelton Ferry	Ark.	201	Dardanelles Lock & Dam	Ark.
049	Lock & Dam No. 3	Ark.	250	Ozark	Ark.
065	Lock & Dam No. 4	Ark.	310	Ft. Smith	Ark.
070	Pine Bluff	Ark.	380	Muskogee	Okla.
085	Lock & Dam No. 5	Ark.	430	Catoosa	Okla.

Ohio River — **Other Rivers** [2]

	Point Pleasant, West Virginia	Huntington, West Virginia	Ashland, Kentucky	Cincinnati, Ohio	Louisville, Kentucky	Owensboro, Kentucky	Evansville, Indiana	Paducah, Kentucky	Fairmont, West Virginia	Morgantown, West Virginia	Brownsville, Pennsylvania	Montgomery, West Virginia	Charleston, West Virginia	Winfield, West Virginia	Calhoun, Kentucky	Knoxville, Tennessee	Chattanooga, Tennessee	Guntersville, Alabama	Decatur, Alabama	Sheffield, Alabama	Carthage, Tennessee	Old Hickory, Tennessee	Nashville, Tennessee	Clarksville, Tennessee	Smithland, Kentucky
Huntington, West Virginia	43																								
Ashland, Kentucky	58	15																							
Cincinnati, Ohio	205	162	147																						
Louisville, Kentucky	338	295	280	133																					
Owensboro, Kentucky	492	449	434	287	154																				
Evansville, Indiana	527	484	469	322	189	35																			
Paducah, Kentucky	669	626	611	464	331	177	142																		
Fairmont, West Virginia	392	435	450	597	730	884	919	1061																	
Morgantown, West Virginia	366	409	424	571	704	858	893	1035	26																
Brownsville, Pennsylvania	321	367	379	529	662	816	851	993	71	45															
Montgomery, West Virginia	85	128	143	290	423	577	612	754	477	451	406														
Charleston, West Virginia	58	101	116	263	396	550	585	727	450	424	379	27													
Winfield, West Virginia	32	75	90	237	370	524	559	701	424	398	353	53	26												
Calhoun, Kentucky	583	540	525	378	245	91	72	214	975	949	904	668	641	615											
Knoxville, Tennessee	1315	1272	1257	1110	977	823	788	650	1707	1681	1636	1400	1373	1347	861										
Chattanooga, Tennessee	1132	1089	1074	927	794	640	605	466	1524	1498	1453	1217	1190	1164	677	184									
Guntersville, Alabama	1026	983	968	821	688	534	499	360	1418	1392	1347	1111	1084	1058	571	290	106								
Decatur, Alabama	972	929	914	767	634	480	445	306	1364	1338	1293	1057	1030	1004	517	343	159	53							
Sheffield, Alabama	922	879	864	717	584	430	395	253	1314	1288	1243	1007	980	954	467	394	210	104	51						
Carthage, Tennessee	964	921	906	759	626	472	437	321	1356	1330	1285	1049	1022	996	509	968	784	678	625	574					
Old Hickory, Tennessee	876	833	818	671	538	384	349	233	1268	1242	1197	961	934	908	421	880	696	590	537	486	88				
Nashville, Tennessee	847	804	789	642	509	355	320	204	1239	1213	1168	932	905	879	392	851	667	561	508	457	117	29			
Clarksville, Tennessee	782	739	724	577	444	290	255	139	1174	1148	1103	867	840	814	327	786	602	496	443	392	182	94	65		
Smithland, Kentucky	658	615	600	453	320	166	131	13	1050	1024	979	743	716	690	203	662	478	372	319	268	306	218	189	124	—

Gulf Intracoastal Waterway West of New Orleans (Industrial Canal Lock)

Brownsville, Texas	Port Isabel, Texas	Corpus Christi, Texas	Aransas Pass, Texas	Port O'Connor, Texas	Port Lavaca, Texas	Freeport, Texas	Houston, Texas	Texas City, Texas	Galveston, Texas	Beaumont, Texas	Port Arthur, Texas	Orange, Texas	Lake Charles, Louisiana	Abbeville, Louisiana (Vermilion Lock)	Morgan City, Louisiana	Port Allen Lock, Louisiana	Old River Lock, Louisiana	Houma, Louisiana	Harvey, Lock, Louisiana
15																			
155	140																		
151	136	16																	
210	195	75	59																
235	220	100	84	25															
291	276	156	140	81	100														
384	369	249	233	174	193	97													
343	328	208	192	133	147	56	59												
329	314	194	178	119	138	42	55	14											
427	412	292	276	217	236	140	143	102	98										
399	384	264	248	189	208	112	115	74	70	28									
420	405	285	269	210	229	133	136	95	91	31	21								
455	440	320	304	245	264	168	171	130	126	66	56	39							
521	506	386	370	311	330	234	237	193	192	132	122	105	90						
588	573	453	437	378	397	301	304	263	259	199	189	172	157	67					
652	637	517	501	442	461	365	368	327	323	263	253	236	221	131	64				
711	696	576	560	501	520	424	427	386	382	322	312	295	280	190	123	74			
627	612	492	476	417	436	340	343	302	298	238	228	211	196	106	39	103	219		
684	669	549	533	474	493	397	400	359	355	295	286	268	253	163	96	130	204	57	
690	675	555	539	480	499	403	406	365	361	301	292	274	259	169	102	136	209	63	6
749	734	614	598	539	558	462	465	424	420	360	351	333	318	228	161	195	269	122	65
765	750	630	614	555	574	478	481	440	436	376	367	349	334	244	177	211	285	138	81
776	761	641	625	566	585	489	492	451	447	387	378	360	345	255	188	222	296	149	92
797	782	662	646	587	606	510	513	472	468	408	399	381	366	276	209	243	317	170	113
847	832	712	696	637	656	560	563	522	518	458	449	431	416	326	259	293	367	220	163
873	858	738	722	663	682	586	589	548	544	484	475	457	442	352	285	319	393	246	189
974	959	839	823	764	783	687	690	649	645	585	576	558	543	453	386	420	494	347	290
1018	1003	883	867	808	827	731	734	693	689	629	620	602	587	497	430	464	538	391	334
1035	1020	900	884	825	844	748	751	710	706	646	637	619	604	514	447	481	555	408	351
1065	1050	930	914	855	874	778	781	740	736	676	667	649	634	544	477	511	585	438	381
1117	1102	982	966	907	926	830	833	792	788	728	719	701	686	596	529	563	637	490	433
1351	1336	1216	1200	1141	1160	1064	1067	1026	1022	962	953	935	920	830	763	797	871	724	667
1363	1348	1228	1212	1153	1172	1076	1079	1038	1034	974	965	947	932	942	775	809	883	736	679
1434	1419	1299	1283	1224	1243	1147	1150	1109	1105	1045	1036	1018	1003	913	846	880	954	807	750
1560	1545	1425	1409	1350	1369	1273	1276	1235	1231	1171	1162	1144	1129	1039	972	1006	1080	933	876
964	949	829	813	754	773	677	680	639	635	575	566	548	533	443	376	410	484	337	280
1063	1048	928	912	853	872	776	779	738	734	674	665	647	632	542	475	509	583	436	379
1186	1171	1051	1035	976	995	899	902	861	857	797	788	770	755	665	598	632	706	559	502
1243	1228	1108	1092	1033	1052	956	959	918	914	854	845	827	812	722	655	689	763	616	559
1263	1248	1128	1112	1053	1072	976	979	938	934	874	865	847	832	742	675	709	783	636	579
1277	1262	1142	1126	1067	1086	990	993	952	948	888	879	861	846	756	689	723	797	650	593

Source: The Intracoastal Waterway—Gulf Section—Corps of Engineers

GULF INTRACOASTAL WATERWAY
and
BLACK WARRIOR, WARRIOR AND TOMBIGBEE SYSTEM

Distance Tables . . . . In Statute Miles

Gulf Intracoastal Waterway East of New Orleans (Industrial Canal) — **Black Warrior, Warrior And Tombigbee River System**

Pass Christian, Mississippi	Gulfport, Mississippi	Biloxi, Mississippi	Pascagoula, Mississippi	Mobile, Alabama	Pensacola, Florida	Panama City, Florida	Port St. Joe, Florida	Apalachicola, Florida	Carrabelle, Florida	St. Marks, Florida	St. Petersburg, Florida	Tampa, Florida	Fort Myers, Florida	Key West, Florida	Jackson, Alabama (Jackson Lock)	Demopolis, Alabama	Tuscaloosa, Alabama	Birminghamport, Alabama	Cordova, Alabama	Sipsey, Alabama
35																				
46	27																			
56	47	40																		
16	97	89	68																	
34	123	116	94	84																
43	223	217	195	185	113															
37	267	261	239	229	157	44														
04	285	278	256	246	174	61	29													
34	315	308	286	276	204	91	59	30												
36	367	360	338	328	256	143	111	82	52											
20	601	594	572	562	490	377	345	316	286	234										
32	613	606	584	574	502	389	357	328	298	246	12									
93	684	677	655	645	573	460	428	399	369	317	83	71								
29	810	803	781	771	699	586	554	525	495	443	209	197	126							
33	214	206	185	117	201	302	346	363	393	445	679	691	762	888						
32	313	305	284	216	300	401	445	462	492	544	778	790	861	987	99					
55	436	428	407	339	423	524	568	585	615	667	901	913	984	1110	222	123				
2	493	485	464	396	480	581	625	642	672	724	958	970	1041	1167	279	180	57			
32	513	505	484	416	500	601	645	662	692	744	978	990	1061	1187	299	200	77	20		
6	527	519	498	430	514	615	659	676	706	758	992	1004	1075	1201	313	214	91	34	14	–

ATLANTIC INTRACOASTAL WATERWAY

Distance Tables . . . . In Statute Miles

Trenton, N.J.	Philadelphia, Pa.	Wilmington, Del.	Baltimore, Md.	Washington, D.C.	Norfolk, Va.	Richmond, Va.	Beaufort, N.C.	Wilmington, N.C.	Georgetown, S.C.	Charleston, S.C.	Savannah, Ga.	Brunswick, Ga.	Fernandina, Fla.	Jacksonville, Fla.	Palatka, Fla.	Ocala, Fla.	Yankeetown, Fla.
33																	
66	33																
135	102	88															
322	289	263	206														
305	272	246	188	204													
390	357	331	274	289	103												
508	475	449	391	407	203	306											
619	586	560	502	517	314	417	111										
711	678	651	594	609	406	509	203	121									
774	741	715	657	673	469	572	266	185	67								
881	857	831	773	788	585	688	382	301	182	116							
990	957	931	873	888	685	788	482	401	282	216	113						
1020	987	961	903	918	715	818	512	431	312	246	142	40					
1063	1031	1005	947	962	759	862	556	475	356	290	186	84	44				
1120	1087	1061	1003	1018	815	918	612	531	412	346	242	140	100	56			
1178	1145	1119	1061	1076	873	976	670	589	470	404	300	198	158	114	58		
1218	1185	1159	1101	1116	913	1016	710	629	510	444	340	238	198	154	98	40	

Source: The Intracoastal Waterway—Atlantic Section—Corps of Engineers

The American Waterways Operators, Inc. (AWO) is a trade association representing the national interests of operators of towboats, tugboats, and barges who provide transport services and ship berthing and other harbor work on the navigable waters of the United States. Our members operate vessels on the inland waterways and over coastal and seagoing routes in all areas of the country. In addition to such vessel operators, AWO also represents shipyards who build and repair the type of equipment operated by our carrier members, terminal operators who serve water carriers, and certain service companies.

The basic policy of the Association is to promote the interests of the inland water carrier industry in such fashion as to make available to the public the benefits made possible by the development of navigable waterways throughout the Nation in times of peace and in times of national emergency. To implement this policy, AWO seeks to influence the course of legislation which affects the interest of shallow-draft water carriers and allied businesses, works with regulatory agencies whose responsibilities affect the interests of its members, and carries out a broad national public relations program.

Listed on the following pages are features of the AWO program which are available to the public as a matter of general interest:

FILM

The American Waterways Operators, Inc. in early 1967 released a documentary movie, THE WONDER OF WATER. This 27-minute, 16 mm color film tells the story of all the public benefits gained in the United States from improvement and use of our water resources, including the benefits in transportation cost savings. How these savings reach right into the home in the form of lower costs for consumer goods and services is shown. The role of the Army Corps of Engineers in providing improvements for our water resources is portrayed. These improvements produce not only transportation benefits; they also produce a wide range of water services—more water where water is needed when it is needed to serve the needs of homes, farms, industry, recreation, and all the other uses to which we put this most precious natural resource. The safety functions of

THE BARGE AND TOWING INDUSTRY ASSOCIATION
W A O

the United States Coast Guard are illustrated. In a beautifully photographed and interestingly narrated movie, the whole scope of the work done to put our U.S. water resources to work for the people is told. These resources are extensive, the most extensive possessed by any nation. They have been put to work well—and THE WONDER OF WATER tells how. The film is available to civic, government, industrial and business groups, and to schools. Bookings may be made through Association-Sterling Films, 866 Third Avenue, New York, New York 10022.

BOOKS AND BROCHURES

BIG LOAD AFLOAT—this descriptive book reports on all phases of barge and towing industry.

INLAND WATERBORNE COMMERCE STATISTICS—a pamphlet published annually giving net tons of traffic and ton-miles of service. Data is compiled from information made available by the Statistical Division of the Board of Engineers for Rivers and Harbors of the Corps of Engineers.

WATERSIDE SITE PLANT LOCATIONS AND EXPANSIONS—a study of industries built, expanded or planned along the inland waterways. Published annually.

UNITED FOR ACTION— A pamphlet published annually which outlines the scope of the industry the Association serves, sets forth AWO's basic operating policies, lists the officers, and gives a brief history of the organization.

MANUALS

BASIC SAFETY PROGRAM FOR BARGE AND TOWING VESSEL INDUSTRY—a manual designed to aid companies and personnel in developing safer work methods and techniques for the industry. As part of this program a monthly safety poster is issued.

INLAND WATERWAYS OPERATORS POLLUTION MANUAL—this publication is designed to bring to the attention of vessel operators and personnel the importance of procedures to prevent pollution of the waterways. A series of pollution posters is a part of this program.

MAPS

THE INLAND WATERWAYS OF THE UNITED STATES—a two-color map showing the commercially navigable inland waterways. Carries a table of authorized depths. Available in two sizes: 11½ inches by 17½ inches and 22 inches by 34 inches.

AWO WEEKLY LETTER

THE PRESS AND ASSOCIATION EDITION is published every Saturday and furnished regularly to editors, college professors of transportation and economics, and other transportation associations and executives, giving them a round-up of information affecting the barge and towing vessel industry during the week. (A Members' edition of the AWO WEEKLY LETTER is also published.)

NEWS RELEASES

NEWS RELEASES are issued whenever warranted on activities of the Association or on other matters affecting the barge and towing vessel industry on which the Association has competence to comment.

Materials and information on the industry are available from the executive offices of The American Waterways Operators, Inc., Suite 502, 1250 Connecticut Avenue, Washington, D. C. 20036. The Association has two field offices: Suite 1408, 17 Battery Place, New York, New York 10004; and Suite 1020, Whitney Building, New Orleans, Louisiana 70130.